Gambling Patient Placement Criteria
GPPC®

A Guide to Placing Problem Gamblers
at the Optimum Level of Care

Denise F. Quirk, Colin Hodgen, Dianne Springborn,
George E. Howell, and Lynne J Daus

Institute for the Study of Gambling & Commercial Gaming
College of Business
University of Nevada, Reno

ISBN-13:   978-0-9796873-2-7

ISBN-10:   0-9796873-2-2

Library of Congress Catalog Card Number 2010928061

Published by
Institute for the Study of Gambling & Commercial Gaming
College of Business
University of Nevada, Reno
1664 N. Virginia St. MS0025
Reno, NV 89557-0025
USA

www.unr.edu/gaming

College of Business
University of Nevada, Reno

Gambling Patient Placement Criteria: GPPC®
A Guide to Placing Problem Gamblers at the Optimum Level of Care
Denise F. Quirk, Colin Hodgen, Dianne Springborn, George E. Howell, and Lynne J Daus

Book design and layout by
Annie Graham Publishing Services
Chattanooga, Tennessee

Printing by
Thomson-Shore, Inc.
Dexter, Michigan

Manufactured and printed in the United States of America

Dedication

There are two pioneers in the treatment of problem gambling who stand out as heroes to the GPPC Team. We will always love Dr. Rena Nora and Dr. Julian Taber for their brilliance, their love of people, their sensitivity to the needs of problem gamblers and families of problem gamblers, their uncomplaining and unending service, their willingness to teach and lead, and for saying "yes" to our invitation to be part of the GPPC Initiative from its inception.

Our minds and hearts have been shaped by the wisdom and experience they shared with us. We are inspired by their sense of adventure and humor, along with the volumes they each published and the many presentations they gave. We are grateful to have sat, listened, and laughed with them. We dedicate this book to the memory of Dr. Rena Nora and Dr. Julian Taber and wish all who read it to study, emulate, and always remember them.

Dr. Rena Nora (1940–2008)

Dr. Julian Taber (1929–2009)

Contents

CD-Rom

Acknowledgments

The creation of the GPPC involved many wonderful people. The following list includes mentors, students, colleagues, friends, and advisors. The GPPC Team invites the reader to celebrate our success by acknowledging the work and creativity of the following individuals:

To Paula Chung, Dani Whittaker, and Bristlecone Family Resources; Mandy Rigsby, Sharon Hay and Ridge House; Kathy Melendy, Paula Williams, Deb Stroud, Richard Deller, and New Frontier Treatment Center; Tom Baltisberger and Robert Meddaugh. We express our gratitude for learning about and implementing the original GPPC tool and giving us valued feedback in our Focus Groups.

To Carol O'Hare, Ken Winters, Tim Christenson, Tim Fong, and Joanna Franklin, for their much appreciated advisement and support.

To Judy Cornelius and the Institute for the Study of Gambling and Commercial Gaming at the University of Nevada, Reno, for endless guidance, editing, and publishing help.

To Janelle Baclayon and the Reno Problem Gambling Center for invaluable administrative and moral support.

To all the members and staff of the State of Nevada's Board of Examiners for Alcohol, Drug and Gambling Counselors for endorsing the GPPC.

To Brian Crane, artist and creator of *Pickles*,™ for the comic relief cartoons in our book.

To the American Society of Addiction Medicine's ASAM PPC-2R for the inspiration and foundation for our research.

And finally, to the members of the Governor's Advisory Committee on Problem Gambling and the Grants Management Unit of the State of Nevada's Health and Human Services Division for their faith and confidence in our project.

Thank you all very much!

About the Authors

Denise F. Quirk has been an addictions counselor and marriage and family therapist in Reno, Nevada since 1992. She is presently the CEO and Clinical Director of the Reno Problem Gambling Center, a non-profit outpatient treatment center for problem gamblers and their families. Denise also serves on the Governor's Advisory Committee for Problem Gambling. She wrote and teaches two online courses on problem gambling for the University of Nevada, Reno. Denise has a private practice, Red Hawk Counseling, in which she does marriage and family therapy, substance abuse, anger management, as well as sex addiction treatment, and does consultation for all problem gambling awareness interests.

Colin Hodgen has a Master's degree in Counseling and Educational Psychology (University of Nevada, Reno, 2005) with an emphasis in Addictions, and is currently a Ph.D. candidate in Counselor Education and Supervision at the University of Nevada, Reno. He is a Nevada Licensed Alcohol and Drug Counselor (LADC), a certified Supervisor of Alcohol and Drug Counselor Interns, a Nevada Certified Problem Gambling Counselor (CPGC) and CPGC Supervisor. He has experience in residential, intensive outpatient, outpatient, continuing care, individual and group counseling, as well as in psychoeducation and the screening, assessment, and appropriate patient placement of individuals with addictive disorders. Colin wrote and teaches an on-line course on Aging and Addictions for the University of Nevada, Reno. Colin provides addictions counseling and consultation services in Reno, Nevada.

George E. Howell is currently the Senior and Outreach Counselor and Program Director for the Reno Problem Gambling Center, an intensive outpatient program for compulsive gamblers. His work includes individual and group counseling, screening and assessments. His experience includes Director of Inpatient Services for a comprehensive alcohol and drug treatment program, inpatient and outpatient Substance Abuse Counselor, DUI and Specialty Court Counselor. He helped establish the Alcohol and Other Drugs Program in Reno Justice and Sparks Municipal Courts. He is a Nevada Licensed Alcohol and Drug Counselor (LADC) and a Certified Supervisor of Alcohol and Drug Counselor Interns (LADC-S). He is a Nevada Certified Problem Gambling Counselor (CPGC). He received his Bachelor's and Master's Degrees from Pepperdine University.

Dianne Springborn has been a therapist since 1982 when she received her Marriage, Family, and Child Counselor's license in California. She has worked in the addiction field in Nevada since 2001. She is a Licensed Clinical Alcohol and Drug Counselor and Supervisor, a Certified Problem Gambling Counselor and Supervisor, and a National Certified Gambling Counselor-II. Dianne has been the Administrator of Bristlecone Family Resources' Gambling Addiction Treatment and Education (GATE) Program for the past five years. She was appointed by the Governor to the Nevada Board of Examiners for Alcohol, Drug and Gambling Counselors in December of 2008.

Lynne J Daus has a Master's degree in Psychology from Antioch University of the West with a minor in chemical dependency (1985) and a Bachelor's degree from the University of California, Santa Barbara (UCSB). She has been a certified drug and alcohol counselor and then a licensed alcohol and drug counselor in the State of Nevada since 1989. Her experience includes inpatient and outpatient treatment. She has been in private practice since 1990 serving alcoholics and addicts and now pathological gamblers. She started taking classes on pathological gambling in 1999 and became a certified problem gambling counselor (CPGC) in 2010. Lynne currently runs an evaluation center and performs assessments for the Reno Problem Gambling Center to assess client placement at the appropriate level of care.

Note to Students, Teachers, and Intern Supervisors

We encourage therapists, counselor interns and supervisors, legal and academic professionals and students to begin your study with the six GPPC dimensions, the four recommended levels of care, the toolkit of forms in the back of the book, and the individual case examples for each dimension and level. These basic elements of a GPPC can provide a basis for discussion and examples for further learning.

The GPPC is very helpful with new counseling students and interns:

- in preparing to interview problem gamblers
- as a way of orienting questions towards determining the immediate and long-term needs of the client in a triage situation and
- as a thorough assessment and diagnosis of pathological gambling and a provisional treatment plan for the client

The GPPC is intended to guide the student, supervisor, intern, legal professional and/or healthcare worker through an optimally determined level of care recommendation for a client.

"Impediment to Treatment or Level of Severity" in the Module section of this manual is of particular importance for those wishing to begin assessing a problem gambling client with the GPPC immediately. We recommend familiarizing yourself with the philosophy of how to quantify your client's needs and symptoms by careful study of this resource and each of the tools in your GPPC toolkit.

This manual was created by an enthusiastic team of expert gambling counselors. We discovered in 2005 that there was no handbook to help counselors properly place gambling clients into the optimal level of care in the same manner as the ASAM PPC-2R did for patients with substance-related disorders. We knew we could combine our experience and ideas to make this happen, and after giving you the very best two years of our time and effort, we give you the GPPC.

We are particularly attuned to the needs of counselor interns and their supervisors. We hope the GPPC will be used to teach and train counselors to become expert assessment and treatment professionals.

The GPPC team has enjoyed discovering the many ways to teach and use the information the GPPC offers. We appreciate your motivation and desire to help others, and thank you for choosing the GPPC. Remember to call or email us with any questions. We are pleased to share our experience with you.

GPPC INITIATIVE OUTREACH AVAILABILITY

The GPPC team is available for assistance, consultation, collaboration, referral, training and outreach. Please feel free to contact us with any questions, comments, and/or suggestions concerning the GPPC and problem gambling treatment. Here's our contact information:

- www.TheGPPC.com
- 1.877.979.4774 (1.877.979.GPPC)
- (775) 284.7234
- (775) 284.5336 fax

Let us know if there's anything we can do to make the GPPC part of your approach to problem gambling screening, assessment, evaluation, treatment planning and treatment, education and support services.

Introduction

The GPPC Initiative is a needs-based, practitioner-tested program to establish a structured and flexible, goal-oriented, focused, individualized, evidence-based, and compatible method of gambling patient placement. The heart of this program is a standardized set of gambling patient placement criteria. Our acronym for these criteria is GPPC (pronounced "gypsy"). The GPPC instrument and its associated "toolkit" provide the necessary tools for qualified practitioners to screen, assess and diagnose disordered gambling, and more significantly, to place the client in a level of care (LOC) of optimal efficacy. This manual contains separate chapters describing applications of the GPPC toolkit beginning with assessment and extending through the recommended levels of care.

The GPPC provides a basis for treatment planning and outcome data evaluation. This capability to link screening and assessment, patient placement, treatment planning, treatment itself, and treatment efficacy has the potential to revolutionize the field. That is, the study and practice of pathological gambling treatment becomes focused and empowered in previously unachievable ways and means.

The GPPC permits accurate, reliable and consistent patient placement. It links screening and assessment with patient placement, tracks adjustments in Levels of Care, tracks client movement in biopsychosocial treatment dimensions, and generates a database for treatment evaluation and research. The GPPC is fully compatible with the American Society of Addiction Medicine's Patient Placement Criteria (currently ASAM PPC-2R) and the American Psychological Association's Diagnostic and Statistical Manual of Mental Disorders (currently DSM-IV). Fundamentally, the GPPC provides structure for the patient placement process. It provides tested tools developed by experienced practitioners in the field for use by other qualified professionals. Moreover, the GPPC provides essential tools for the training and supervision of gambling counselor interns.

Nationwide, 6 to 9 million people (3–4% of adults) met criteria for a gambling problem, with an estimated social cost to families and communities from gambling-related bankruptcy, divorce, crime and job loss of almost $7 billion within the last year (National Council on Problem Gambling, 2009). In Nevada, the prevalence of problem/pathological gambling among adults is almost 7% and up to 9.9% can be classified as "at risk" gamblers (Volberg, 2002).

With these rates of prevalence and incidence of disordered gambling, the need for qualified prevention/treatment professionals has never been greater. Similarly, the need for coherent, consistent, evidence-based screening and assessment, patient placement, and treatment is urgent. This is exactly what we offer with the Gambling Patient Placement Criteria. We strongly encourage you to try the GPPC toolkit in your own practice. We sincerely solicit your feedback on its effectiveness.

How GPPC Works

The GPPC Manual

The GPPC Manual contains chapters arranged chronologically—from screening through treatment—as well as hierarchically—from lowest level of care to highest. Here is the layout:

- GPPC Screening and Assessment
- GPPC Level 0.5 Early Intervention Services
- GPPC Level I Outpatient Services
- GPPC Level II Intensive Outpatient Services
- GPPC Level III Residential Treatment Services
- Family and Legal Issues
- Treatment Planning and Treatment

The chapters are designed to be used separately for specific applications as well as collectively for addressing broader issues and techniques across the continuum of care.

The Levels of Care (LOC) chapters are laid out in a consistent format of an introductory vignette, a general discussion, a prototypical case study and an example of a completed GPPC appropriate to the level of care and case study. The discussions are structured in a format adapted from the Colorado Prevention Leadership Council.

The GPPC Manual also includes an extensive bibliography and a list of recommended readings for use by those wishing more extensive information on pathological gambling and its treatment. As well, the manual provides information on how to contact The GPPC Initiative, the team of treatment professionals who developed the GPPC and who are available for training and community outreach concerning pathological gambling and the application of the various GPPC tools.

The GPPC Toolkit

The Gambling Patient Placement Criteria (GPPC) described in this manual provides a simple set of tools to assist caring professionals working with problem gamblers. The GPPC Form is the fundamental component of this toolkit. It offers a "roadmap" to guide the clinician in collecting information from the client in order to make informed decisions about the severity of the client's presenting problems and possible options for patient placement and treatment. This form can be used as a simple screening checklist, as the basis for extended assessment and as the outline for a comprehensive narrative evaluation. The GPPC can not only guide the assessment and placement process, it can also provide structure in initial treatment planning, and can be used periodically throughout treatment to document the client's progress. The GPPC can also be used to provide data to track overall treatment program outcomes and efficacy as well as data for extended research and analysis in the field of pathological gambling.

The GPPC toolkit contains the fundamental building blocks for determining optimal patient placement, that is, the basic necessities for accurately, reliably and consistently structuring client screening, assessment, placement, and treatment. Here are the basic tools:

- The GPPC Template (in computer and paper formats)
- "Using the GPPC" (a step-by-step guide for filling out the form)

- The GPPC Counselor Working Aid (guidance, suggestions and hints for essential elements of information to consider when making clinical judgments in problem gambling placement and treatment)
- The GPPC Levels of Severity Scale (to gauge the relative severity or urgency of the client's presenting problems, the estimated or recommended intensity of treatment and the estimated relative impediment to treatment these problems may pose for the client and clinician)
- The GPPC Levels of Care (recommended levels based on the scope and intensity of treatment extending from Early Intervention through Residential Treatment)
- Screening and Assessment Instruments (recommended instruments to consider or include in determining the severity of the disorder and the recommended level of treatment)
    - The American Psychiatric Association Diagnostic and Statistical Manual of Mental Disorders (4th edition) (DSM-IV) Criteria
    - The Gamblers Anonymous (GA) 20 Questions
    - The National Opinion Research Center (NORC) DSM-IV Screen for Gambling Problems (NODS)
    - The South Oaks Gambling Screen (SOGS)
- Suicidality and Harm risk ratings
    - The San Francisco Suicide Prevention Risk Assessment "PLAID PALS"
    - The American Society of Addiction Medicine Patient Placement Criteria (2nd edition, revised) (ASAM PPC-2R) Risk Ratings
- Examples of completed GPPC assessment narratives (computer and paper versions)

All of these tools are provided in the Module section of the GPPC Manual and are included on the accompanying compact disc (GPPC-CD). We hope you will find these tools useful in daily practice, in academic or research applications, or as a component of counselor intern supervision.

More Will Be Revealed

The GPPC Manual is a work in progress. This first publication is the result of two years of effort and the initial implementation of the GPPC by practitioners in Nevada. The next phase consists of a number of continuing initiatives. One of these efforts is broader dissemination of the GPPC to caring professionals working in prevention, evaluation, treatment and research concerning problem gambling. Another effort is extended outreach to professionals and concerned individuals in related fields such as social services, education, regulatory and legislative organizations and the criminal justice system. The GPPC Initiative is also involved in incorporating the GPPC toolkit into a statewide data management system used by Nevada substance abuse prevention and treatment agencies, the Nevada Health Information Provider Performance System (NHIPPS.) This alliance will extend and improve the ability to screen, place and treat problem gamblers with co-occurring substance-related disorders.

Some simple, preliminary statistical results of the initial 100 GPPC reports are displayed in the Module section in the back of this book. It will be understood best in context once the reader has read and worked through this manual.

A Word about Our Case Studies

These case studies are purely notional and are formulated to provide a context for presenting issues, circumstances and situations which may be representative of those faced by problem gamblers. The identities, life circumstances and presenting problems are purely fictitious, synthesized from the experiences of a variety of problem gambling counselors, problem gamblers and their families, and scholars in the field of addictions. Any resemblance, however slight, to any person or persons, living or dead, is purely coincidental and unintended. While we may refer to organizations or institutions such as Gamblers Anonymous or various financial institutions or gaming venues, we do not presume to speak for those organizations and do not represent any association between those organizations and the GPPC Initiative.

These notional scenarios or vignettes may be useful for students or interns who wish to practice doing a GPPC assessment or evaluation, drawing from the case studies to find elements they wish to include in filling out the GPPC form or in forming their clinical impressions of a representative fictitious client at a particular level of care.

I
GPPC® Screening and Assessment

Vignette

Iris Kitall is a woman who was very successful in her sales and investment business, who did quite well for herself and her family. However, after 40 years in business, she was arrested by the Federal Bureau of Investigation and sent to prison for fraud. She has a history of gambling in casinos, but denies that it is a problem. She states she has never gambled more than she intended, and committed the illegal act because "the people I was working for did not give me credit for the work I did." She was very sorry for putting her husband through all the heartache brought along with going to prison for five years and losing her career and money. She does not think she needs any counseling. After reviewing her GPPC and getting releases to speak with her probation officer and her family, you discover that she actually has a serious gambling problem, even though she does not agree. Your client will need a formal intervention. If you can get the family, the Probation Officer and the client in the same room at the same time to discuss the problem, you may motivate your client to participate in treatment.

As the counselor, what would you do?

Discussion

Problem Statement

Pathological gambling, an impulse control disorder, as with other behavioral or process addictions, can be very difficult to detect in early stages, even by trained professionals. Behavioral or process addictions can be "invisible" in the early stages, and often remain largely ignored, overlooked, or tolerated until the occurrence of some precipitating crisis. The result can be some personal calamity (bankruptcy, foreclosure, arrest, etc.) with collateral damage to others. Pathological gambling often occurs as part of a cluster of co-occurring disorders (substance abuse, mood disorder, etc.) which may mask or obscure the gambling activity that may have contributed to these and other disorders. This is especially true at the outer edges of the age spectrum of "average" clients, that is, among adolescents and older adults, who are particularly vulnerable to problem gambling.

It is extremely important that caring professionals such as physicians, psychologists, social workers, marriage and family therapists, drug and alcohol counselors, domestic violence risk assessors, or any other mental health specialists be aware of the risk for pathological gambling among their clients and have a simple set of tools for screening, assessment, and/or referral.

The GPPC toolkit contains a selection of instruments for the screening, assessment, evaluation, and diagnosis of pathological gambling. The GPPC form itself documents the use and results of these instruments and assists in determining the optimum level of care, placement and treatment approach for an individual client. These instruments are effective individually or in combination with other diagnostic tools.

Contributing Factors

When a client schedules an appointment for a gambling assessment it may be clear what the client is asking for. However, it may be unclear what the client is actually willing to do to get help or to change behaviors. The client may be self-referred or seek treatment at the recommendation of an Employee Assistance Program, another mental health provider or a legal referral. The evaluator will want empirical, clinical evidence of the extent and severity of the disorder using standard validated assessment instruments allowing reliable documentation of the results. It is important to do a thorough assessment to facilitate correct placement at the appropriate level of care. Despite the referral source, or the client's stage of change, it is always important to refer the client to the appropriate level of care as indicated by the screening results and the evaluator's clinical judgment. Even if the client shows up presenting with a different problem, screening with the Lie-Bet Questionnaire (Johnson, et al., 1998) will indicate whether the client needs a gambling assessment. With the GPPC the provider can assess clients for gambling problems or refer them to a credentialed problem gambling professional for a more comprehensive assessment.

Intended Outcome

A complete assessment using the GPPC provides reliable documentation describing the disorder for use by the client and clinician, the client's referral source, a gambling treatment provider or other mental health professional as well as for accurate information for insurance billing purposes. A good assessment provides a baseline for measuring change and gives an accurate view of the client's level of functioning (McCown and Howatt, 2007).

A good assessment not only collects and organizes significant information on behalf of the client and the practitioner; it also "evaluates an individual's strengths, weaknesses, problems and needs, and determines priorities so that a treatment plan can be developed" (ASAM PPC-2R, p. 359) and guides the placement of the client in an appropriate level of care. A good assessment can also help the client gain insight in two ways: 1) it helps bring to light the extent of the client's problem gambling, and 2) it provides hope that there is help for the client and that the client can change with professional help.

One of the simplest yet most effective screening tools, the Lie-Bet Questionnaire consists of two items:
- "Have you ever had to lie to people important to you about how much you gambled?"
- "Have you ever felt the need to bet more and more money?"

This simple screening takes less than a minute as part of any other health screening by health care and mental health care professionals and non-professional or non-credentialed care givers. The reliability and validity of the Lie-Bet Questionnaire has an internal sensitivity of .99 and a specificity of .91. Answering "Yes" to one or both questions strongly suggests problem gambling and the need for further assessment by a credentialed professional qualified to diagnose and/or treat pathological gambling (Johnson, et al., 1998).

Evidence-Based Programs/Services

The GPPC toolkit includes several instruments for more formal assessment, evaluation, and/or diagnosis (See GPPC Manual Module). These instruments include the DSM-IV diagnostic criteria, the Gamblers Anonymous 20 questions, the University of Chicago's National Opinion Research Center (NORC) DSM-IV Screen for Gambling Problems (NODS), and the South Oaks Gambling Screen (SOGS). Although not included in the GPPC toolkit, we also recommend the Massachusetts Gambling Screen (MAGS) and the Substance Abuse Subtle Screening Inventory-3 (SASSI-3) for use in the screening and assessment of potential problem gamblers.

Practitioners may choose to use one or more of the screening and assessment instruments included in the GPPC toolkit. Some of these instruments and questions may appear to be redundant, specifically, the DSM-IV diagnostic criteria and the NODS. Why use different instruments that ask the same questions? It has been our clinical observation and experience that clients often respond to these questions differently. The NODS, of course, is predicated on the DSM criteria, so the instruments do indeed seek to identify the presence or absence of the same diagnostic criteria for the disorder. However, clients may tend to answer one set of questions one way, with more negative answers to the questions, and then answer the opposite way on the other questionnaire with more positive responses. It is unclear if this is part of the denial process or an indicator that the pathological gambler's thinking is so disordered that processing information is difficult and produces dissimilar responses.

The Substance Abuse Subtle Screening Inventory (SASSI-3), while not included in the GPPC toolkit, is highly recommended when assessing a potential problem gambler. Again, our observations and experience suggest the majority of pathological gamblers have unrecognized or untreated substance-related disorders. The presence and severity of these disorders may interfere with successful treatment of pathological gambling. Co-occurring or concurrent disorders are best dealt with as part of a comprehensive screening and assessment just as they must be dealt with as part of a comprehensive, holistic treatment plan. The clinician can make the best possible use of a screening/assessment opportunity, thereby helping clients recognize the scope and interaction of their problematic behaviors. Identifying multiple disorders in one session permits early inclusion of additional treatment professionals as part of the treatment team.

It will be extremely difficult for a client with alcohol dependence who is still actively drinking to stop disordered gambling if alcohol is part of the gambling pattern. Similarly, a client with bipolar disorder may be unable to resist gambling during the manic phase if the disorder is undiagnosed or untreated. Moreover, if problem gambling only occurs during manic episodes, the client may not in fact meet diagnostic criteria for pathological gambling.

Services and Target Populations

Screening, assessment and evaluation is appropriate for clients voluntarily seeking assistance with a perceived gambling problem, clients referred by other health care or mental health care professionals, or by the criminal justice system.

It is important that the person performing a thorough problem gambling assessment be appropriately credentialed. Some examples are Nationally Certified Gambling Counselor (NCGC), International Certified Gambling Counselor (ICGC), or in some states, Certified Problem Gambling Counselor (CPGC) and/or CPGC-Intern (CPGC-I). Other licensed professionals such as Psychologists, Marriage and Family Therapists (MFT), or Licensed Clinical Social Workers (LCSW), who are thoroughly trained in pathological gambling, can also provide these assessments and diagnoses. The GPPC can aid in providing a thorough assessment tool and in providing supervisors with a great teaching aid in training interns on how to perform a comprehensive biopsychosocial gambling assessment.

A comprehensive assessment for problem gambling can take from one to two hours, based on the instruments used and how long it takes the client to fill out forms and respond to interview questions. The GPPC form works as a guide for a structured assessment interview, to record the results of an unstructured biopsychosocial interview, or as an *aide-mémoire* for historical/chronological interviews. The GPPC can assist in collecting pertinent demographic information; assessing the severity of various biopsychosocial dimensions; enumerating initial clinical impressions; recording consents, releases, and referrals; developing provisional treatment planning and discharge criteria; documenting the date, place and time of the interview; and listing the name and credentials of the interviewer/counselor and/or counselor supervisor. These data can provide the foundation for a more formal or extensive comprehensive assessment or evaluation, based on the needs of the client. In order to be able to assess a client for the proper level of care, the evaluator must first consider all GPPC dimensions and then evaluate the relative severity or impediment to treatment in terms of these dimensions and the overall implications for treatment. Level of care and treatment approach are driven by the relative significance of these dimensional problems individually and as part of the comprehensive presenting problem. The GPPC Counselor Working Aid (see GPPC Manual Module) contains guidance, prompts, and examples for use of the GPPC during assessment.

Evaluation

Comparison of a client's Initial, Review, and Discharge GPPC forms can be useful for the practitioner to evaluate the efficacy or "success" of treatment on an individual basis. For practitioners to evaluate programmatic efficacy or success on a much broader scale, a more comprehensive set of tools is often required. Although not included in the GPPC toolkit, a much more extensive and comprehensive package of instruments for identifying agency or program problems at intake, aiding with treatment referral decisions, assisting with treatment planning, for determining aftercare needs, and for evaluating client and/or significant-other progress post-treatment, as well as overall treatment program efficacy, is the Gambling Treatment Outcome Monitoring System (GAMTOMS) (Stinchfield, R., Winters, K.C., Botzet, A., Jerstad, S., and Breyer J., 2007).

Agency Capacity

An assessment/evaluation agency requires one or more credentialed professionals qualified to assess, evaluate and diagnose pathological gambling. This requires specialized training in the disorder in addition to training and experience in the performance of valid screening, assessment and evaluation. Treatment agencies will normally have credentialed professionals on staff who are qualified to perform this function. Agencies providing treatment for other addictive disorders and many general social services providers may have to refer their clients to qualified, credentialed problem gambling professionals for appropriate client screening, assessment and evaluation.

Collaboration

Credentialed professionals performing problem gambling screening, assessment and evaluation will by necessity collaborate with other mental health care, primary health care, social service providers, treatment providers, elements of the criminal justice and court system, and other community agencies. This is an important part of treatment. Assessors/evaluators can provide a great deal of direct and indirect support to the client and clinician by being knowledgeable about available treatment resources, locally, regionally, and nationally. Close cooperation and collaboration among and between all partners in the treatment team optimizes the opportunity for treatment success. This is particularly true in the instance of mandated assessments and evaluations.

Mandated Assessments and Evaluations

One similarity between addiction counseling and problem gambling counseling trends is the movement to allow pathological gamblers who have committed crimes to support their addiction to enter court-ordered diversion programs. In the 1970s and 1980s, most people in alcoholism and drug addiction treatment were there because they wanted to be there. Family or friends might have motivated those clients, but court-ordered treatment was rare. Since the 1990s an increasing number of the people in both residential and outpatient treatment are either mandated by the court or are in treatment to reduce their legal problems. Probation officers, lawyers, and judges have experience with clients being successful in these programs. These diversion programs are part of the new trend of implementing programs to help pathological gamblers in the criminal justice system get treatment. Both New York and Nevada (Nevada Revised Statutes, NRS 458A, "Prevention and Treatment of Problem Gambling") have enacted such legislation. Early intervention has helped the alcoholic and addict and it can help the pathological gambler.

The GPPC Form

*The **GPPC** Header*

The GPPC Header box allows the practitioner to gather pertinent demographic data quickly and easily. This information is useful for client tracking as well as for research and analysis of client data. Demographic and severity data can be used for evaluating treatment outcomes and effectiveness. Note that severity data in the various dimensions can be documented for prior assessments or conditions as well as for current assessments or conditions. For further guidance on rating severity levels, refer to "Impediment to Treatment or Level of Severity" (see GPPC Manual Module). For preliminary research on the first 100 GPPCs collected in Nevada, visit the web site www.thegppc.com.

Dimension 1: Frequency/Intensity/Duration of Disorder

Dimension 1 is focused on the presenting problem of pathological gambling and is a subjective/objective rating of what the DSM-IV refers to as "clinically significant impairment or distress" resulting from "persistent and recurrent maladaptive gambling behavior." In this dimension, the practitioner considers how long the client has been gambling, when it became a problem for the client, how often and how much the client gambles, the progression of gambling behavior over time, and the financial impact of gambling. As described in the GPPC Counselor Working Aid (see GPPC Manual Module), this is what we call "getting the client's drift," using the acronym DRIFT to include the elements of Duration, Recurrence, Intensity, Financial impact, and Type of gambling. As a rule, the greater the severity of the disorder, the higher the level of recommended treatment or the greater the urgency of intervention.

Dimension 2: Biomedical Conditions/Complications

Pathological gamblers will often present with co-occurring health problems. These may be a result of, or complicated by, gambling and may present a complication or impediment to treatment. Severe health conditions and/or the need for certain medications may preclude certain levels or intensities of treatment. It is important to get some indication of the client's health history, current condition, and treatment compliance and consider how that might influence placement and treatment. For example, a client requiring daily dialysis treatments may be unable to comply with the conditions of intensive outpatient or residential treatment. A client in relatively good overall health may be able to comply with whatever level of care is otherwise indicated.

Dimension 3: Cognitive/Behavioral/Emotional Conditions

Most treatment protocols for pathological gambling incorporate some amount of cognitive-behavioral therapy. It is important to document insofar as possible the client's history and current condition in the cognitive, behavioral, and emotional domains. Minimally, these include prior/current learning disabilities, legal history, mood disorders, and other mental health issues. Family history in these areas may also contribute to, complicate, or impede treatment. Refer to the GPPC Counselor Working Aid (see GPPC Manual Module) for specific topics of concern in this dimension and consider how they might affect treatment at various levels of care.

Dimension 4: Readiness to Change

The client's readiness or willingness to change is an important consideration in treatment placement. Unwillingness or resistance to change can present a significant impediment to treatment. It may be useful to consider the client's readiness to change with reference to the Stages of

Change model (see the Chart Module). Additional guidance on rating Dimension 4 is contained in the GPPC Counselor Working Aid and Impediment to Treatment or Level of Severity forms in the GPPC Manual Module. The Stages of Change model also can be used to track the client's movement within and between these stages. Note here that a client who is very ready and willing to change will normally present a low impediment to treatment, thus a lower numerical severity rating. The severity level in this case would be rated lower than a client who is not at all ready or willing to change. Our vignette of Iris Kitall presents a person with a significant impediment to treatment (denial) and would be rated much higher in severity than the ready and willing client. As with all other rated dimensions, the practitioner must consider the relative severity of the condition and/or the degree of impediment to treatment that the condition may present. When asking questions, remember to use Motivational Interviewing/Enhancement techniques to help determine the client's motivation and desire to change. One of the most important questions is "What is going to be the best thing about stopping gambling?" The client may answer in two ways: one answer may be about the money and the other answer, perhaps the most important, will be about the client's personal future. This question will allow the clinician to discover the client's ability to grasp the hope for recovery. This vision of the future provides hope to the client. It will also give an understanding of what is important to the client and why the client wants to make life changes.

Dimension 5: Relapse or Continued Problem History or Potential

Level of care placement and treatment planning must be responsive to the relapse history and/or potential of the client. A client with frequent relapse history or with high relapse potential will likely require more intensive treatment interventions at a higher level of care than will a client with no such history. Relapse prevention education and training is an essential component of treatment at all levels and is a critical factor in continuing care and recovery planning post-treatment. The status of any co-occurring disorders is an important factor in determining relapse potential, placement, and treatment.

Dimension 6: Current Recovery/Living Environment

Treatment extends beyond the treatment locale. It is important to determine where the client returns to or will return to upon completion of separate treatment sessions or at the completion of the overall treatment program. A client who returns to old playgrounds, old playthings, and old playmates is at much greater risk of problems in treatment and longer term recovery than a client who returns to a helpful, hopeful, and supportive recovery environment. Continuing care and recovery planning are based largely on the relative severity of the current and projected recovery environment. Referral to appropriate social services can be a useful adjunct to placement, treatment, and discharge planning.

Driving Dimensions

Driving dimensions are those of most immediate concern or urgency and are important factors in determining level of care placement and treatment approach during a particular phase of treatment. Driving dimensions may change over the course of treatment.

Use the GPPC to organize all of this information, and then score each GPPC dimension. If the client scores high in only one dimension, this person would most likely benefit from a Level 1 program. If the client scores high in two or three dimensions, this person would most likely benefit from a Level 2 program. If the client scores high in three, four or five dimensions, this person may require residential or inpatient treatment if available.

These are general guidelines only. There is no substitute for informed clinical judgment and the immediate needs of the client.

Suicidality; Threat to Self/Others

Pathological gamblers are at significantly higher risk of suicidal or anti-social behaviors. This is a key consideration in level of care placement and treatment approach; equally in discharge planning and continuing care. The GPPC toolkit includes a suicidality screening tool based on the acronym "PLAID PALS" (see Screening/Assessment Instruments Module). Assessors/evaluators may wish to include or consider including ASAM PPC-2R Risk Ratings (R0–R4), also included in the Screening/Assessment Instruments Module

Vulnerabilities/Strengths

A useful assessment/evaluation will not only include the difficulties or disorders affecting the client, but will also include those factors which support or strengthen the client and can contribute to more positive treatment outcomes. A client with greater biopsychosocial "assets" may likely require a lower level of care and less intensive treatment interventions.

Assessment Instruments Used and Results

Use of valid/reliable assessment instruments contributes to the objectivity of an assessment and can reduce the intentional/unintentional effects of subjective influences. Good instrumentation combined with good clinical judgment can contribute to the structural integrity of the assessment. Documenting the results of various instruments is important at initial and continuing assessment for level of care placement and treatment planning. For assessments to be read by non-professionals, describe the results of the instruments used and include the name of the instrument, the client's score, and the criteria employed to make the assessment. When reporting results of the DSM Gambling Screen, the NORC DSM-IV Screen for Gambling Problems (NODS), and the South Oaks Gambling Screen (SOGS), make it apparent to the reader that 5 or more "Yes" answers on any of the above instruments indicates probable pathological gambling. If reporting results on the Gamblers Anonymous (GA) 20 Questions indicate that 7 or more "Yes" answers on this survey suggests probable compulsive gambling. Terminology and threshold levels for the above instruments are included in the Screening/Assessment Instruments Module. When reporting a SASSI-3 score for the client, include a statement on whether the client has a high or low probability of substance dependence, along with the individual scales and explanations for each. If the assessment counselor chooses to utilize another assessment tool, include those results, and their diagnostic significance, in this section.

Clinical Impressions

The Clinical Impressions section of the GPPC permits the practitioner to combine the subjective and objective elements of the assessment interview in terms of the practitioner's observation and experience. Assessment instruments provide the "science" of the assessment; clinical impressions provide the "art." Many practitioners include, and we recommend, the Multiaxial Assessment format drawn from the American Psychiatric Association's Diagnostic and Statistical Manual of Mental Disorders (DSM-IV). Use of the GPPC during assessment greatly facilitates this process and facilitates treatment matching using American Society of Addiction Medicine patient placement criteria (currently ASAM PPC-2R). GPPC is fully compatible with, and bridges the gap between, these widely accepted classification systems with specific regard to the pathological gambler.

Reports Made; Consents Given

An unread assessment is of little use to the client or practitioner. However, assessment and evaluation reports must be protected and read only by those to whom the client has given permission or release. It is very important to fully and accurately document what information is released and to whom on behalf of the client. This protects the client and the practitioner. In writing reports for the court, assessors/evaluators should exercise extra care and discretion. Client information collected during an assessment for problem gambling, as opposed to an assessment of alcohol and drug abuse, is not currently protected under the provisions of the U.S. Code of Federal Regulations (CFR), Title 42, Part 2, which regulates the confidentiality of alcohol and drug abuse patient records. Inadvertent disclosure in an assessment of illegal or illicit acts committed by the gambler to support problem gambling (a diagnostic criterion) may violate the client's right to protection against self-incrimination. Such information could be used against the client in court if included in evaluations and routine reports. It is important, of course, to provide the court with the identifying information and clinical information that supports the diagnosis of pathological gambling, but without providing any potentially self-incriminating information or disclosures by the client. Assure that appropriate client consent is obtained before any reports or communications are made on behalf of the client.

Provisional Treatment Plan & Discharge/Transition Criteria

Where possible, and when qualified, the assessor may wish to provide some preliminary or provisional treatment planning and discharge criteria. At a minimum this will include the initial recommended treatment and/or level of care, the likely duration or schedule of treatment and what will be involved in determining movement from one level of care to another.

Become familiar with the residential and other treatment programs around your state, region, and country. If the client appears to require residential level treatment, but absolutely cannot go to residential treatment, then the treatment plan at a lower level of care may need to be intensified to include more support. This is especially true when the only available treatment consists of weekly individual or group sessions.

Disposition/Follow-up/Appointment/Re-interview

The assessor/evaluator should document the outcome/disposition of the assessment, any follow-up by the client or the evaluator, any appointments made as part of the assessment, and the need for any re-interview to complete the assessment process.

Referrals

The assessor/evaluator should document any referrals made as part of the assessment, including, whenever possible, the name of the agency or individual from whom or to whom the client is referred.

Additional Information

The assessor should document the name and credentials of the assessor/evaluator as well as the date, time and place of assessment.

Counselor/Supervisor Signatures

The assessor, and when necessary, the counselor's supervisor, should sign and date the assessment.

II
GPPC® Level 0.5
Early Intervention Services

Vignette

A Typical GPPC Level 0.5 Early Intervention Services Client

Will Wager is a 58-year-old, single White male living in Reno, Nevada. The client is seeking treatment for concerns related to several recent gambling episodes. He reports losing over $1,100 in two weeks recently while playing video gaming machines in a local casino, money he could not afford to lose. Will reports he has never gambled, or been exposed to it, prior to his arrival in Reno six months ago. He reports little knowledge or understanding of gambling in general or of casino table games. Will reports his initial experiences with video games were "exciting, interesting, and fun." He reports having won over $500 during his first week of casino play. Will soon began playing larger amounts on video gaming machines and found it even more exciting. As his frequency and amount of play increased, he began drawing on his retirement income and savings to continue to play. Will now reports he lost money he needs for his university tuition while playing video games. His retirement check and G.I. Bill student stipend will arrive at the end of the month, but for now he feels worried about "scraping by" until the end of the month.

Discussion

This Level of Care (LOC) consists of gambling-related psychoeducation and information services for a variety of populations and purposes. This LOC also provides brief intervention services for those at risk for problem or pathological gambling and/or those with prodromal or early-stage problem gambling. LOC 0.5 also includes gambling-related community outreach services to other mental health and social service providers, members of the gaming industry, academic institutions, and other interested parties.

Problem Statement

Legalized, commercial gambling, or gaming, is an increasingly pervasive social activity. Its popularity and proliferation raise numerous concerns among a variety of social, political, commercial and governmental factions. A key consideration is how to identify and reduce any potential negative social consequences of what, for many, is a relatively harmless recreational activity.

One of the often hidden costs of legalized gambling is the potential human cost for those affected by problem or pathological gambling. One strategy for approaching this issue is to offer psychoeducation and early intervention programs to selected communities, groups and individuals. Psychoeducation and early intervention programs offer varying levels of focus and intensity based on the needs of involved parties, at the lowest or least invasive Level of Care (LOC).

GPPC LOC 0.5 services are appropriate for communities, groups, families, and individuals who want or need more information about present or potential problem gambling. That is, they may have a gambling problem or concern and not know what to do about it themselves or who to contact for information and assistance. LOC 0.5 is very broad in scope, can be tailored to the particular needs or interests of the client or target audience, and includes but is not limited to:

1. Definition/Description of Gambling, Problem Gambling, Pathological Gambling
2. Models of Addiction and Impulse Control Disorders
3. Genetics of Addiction; Dysfunctional Family
4. Progression of the Disorder
5. Treatments for Disordered Gambling
6. Progression of Recovery
7. Relapse Prevention & Continuing Care
8. Family Recovery
9. Community Action

LOC 0.5 also may be used to provide interim services to a client awaiting placement at a higher level of care.

Contributing Factors

Numerous factors contribute to the proliferation of gambling, and many social factors mitigate for or against it. The fact is, gambling in one form or another is here to stay. For many communities, commercial gambling is an important source of revenue and employment. There are, however, significant risk factors associated with gambling which may not be widely understood. In general, accessibility has been a key risk factor, in that proximity to gaming venues tends to increase prevalence and incidence of gambling. Gambling is also well associated with the use of tobacco and alcohol. Psychoeducation and early intervention can be part of a comprehensive social response to activities perceived to put members of society at risk. In addition to alcohol and tobacco use and proximity and accessibility to gaming venues, age, gender, and other demographic factors are becoming linked to problem gambling.

Intended Outcomes

Intended outcomes for this Level of Care include raising community, group and individual awareness of gambling and potential associated negative effects. This incorporates known and emerging risk and protective factors for problem gambling, warning signs and symptoms of a developing disorder, the availability of treatment, and relapse prevention strategies for those at identifiable risk of persistent problem or pathological gambling. As above, psychoeducation and early intervention can be offered at various levels of focus and intensity from the community level to the individual.

Evidence-based Programs/Services

Current research and practice support various treatment approaches, most using a cognitive-behavioral approach. Research suggests clients with appropriate and valid, factual information may tend to make better, more effective decisions to guide their behavior. Psychoeducation is largely cognitive in its orientation. Early-intervention is probably the least intensive or invasive form of a behavioral approach to treatment.

Services and Target Populations

Psychoeducation and early intervention are primarily information-driven activities involving lectures, briefings, panel discussions, community roundtables, group discussions, and individually delivered information and processing sessions. It is appropriate for four broad applications: Universal, Selective, Indicated and Mandated interventions.

Universal psychoeducation is designed to be offered to all members of a particular population, e.g., members of a local community, mental health professionals, counselor educators, etc. A community already with, or considering offering, legalized commercial gambling would benefit from a variety of information about problem gambling.

Selective psychoeducation is appropriate for particular members of a group who are, or may be, at elevated risk for problem gambling, e.g., casino employees, lottery operators, adolescents, college students and older adults.

Indicated psychoeducation is appropriate for individuals who already display signs of the problem, e.g., someone beginning to experience episodic impairment or distress as a result of gambling. Preliminary screening of these individuals may reveal sub-clinical or clinical pathological gambling.

Mandated psychoeducation is appropriate for individuals referred by the criminal justice system for introductory psychoeducation and intervention. These clients may have been involved in writing bad checks, credit defaults, or embezzlement to cover gambling debts.

Evaluation

The best measure of the effectiveness of psychoeducation and early intervention is a reduction in high-risk behaviors and in negative consequences associated with gambling. These can be community, group, family, or individual consequences and generally are reported as improved quality of life for the individual, family or community. An individual may remark, "I feel better about myself and my behaviors." Civic leaders may feel more engaged and empowered by learning about positive prevention and early-intervention initiatives targeting potential problem gambling in the community.

Agency Capacity

Agency capacity is largely dependent on the target population. Agencies operating at the community level benefit from extended contact with other social agencies within the community. Level 0.5 is a flexible delivery procedure, easily adaptable to available facilities in the agency and community. Prevention and early-intervention programs are probably the most effective use of limited staff and facility resources. For example, one trained professional can provide a great deal of information to a larger population through lectures, community presentations, discussion groups, information briefings, video presentations, and other opportunities to disseminate information. Level 0.5 may become more personnel-intensive as the number of participants becomes more limited, progressing to one-on-one sessions with interested or affected individuals.

Collaboration

This level of care also provides an opportunity for the practitioner to build working alliances with other mental health providers, social services providers, concerned citizens, and civic groups who may have questions, concerns, or involvement with matters concerning gambling within the community. Credentialed problem gambling counselors can provide much needed subject-matter expertise on issues of prevention, intervention and treatment for individuals affected by gambling.

Summary

GPPC Level 0.5, Early Intervention Services, is a flexible, low intensity, low overhead treatment approach for clients experiencing early signs of problem gambling. It is easily tailored to individuals, couples, small groups, and community organizations with concerns about the effects of gambling. It may also provide interim services while a client waits for admission into a higher level of care.

Case Study

The client, Will Wager, is a 58-year-old, single White male living in Reno, Nevada. He has concerns related to several recent disturbing gambling episodes. Will recently retired from the U.S. military after 30 years of service and moved from New England to Reno to attend the University of Nevada, Reno (UNR) on the G.I. Bill to obtain a Master's degree. He reports losing over $1,100 in two weeks recently while playing video gaming machines in a local casino; money he could not afford to lose. Will denies prior or current medical or health concerns. He smokes cigarettes, up to one pack per day. Will reports prior history of, and residential treatment for, alcohol dependence, but has been in active recovery for over 18 years. He denies other history of mental health treatment. Will denies prior or current, juvenile or adult criminal history or incarceration. He denies prior or current episodes of verbal, emotional, physical, and/or sexual (VEPS) abuse as a child or adult and denies being a victim or perpetrator of domestic violence.

Mr. Wager reports he has never gambled, or been exposed to it, prior to his arrival in Reno six months ago. He previously played once per week, but has not gambled in two weeks. He reports little knowledge or understanding of gambling in general or of casino table games. Will states his initial experiences with video games were "exciting, interesting, and fun." He reports having won over $500 during his first week of casino play. He soon began playing larger amounts on video gaming machines and found it even more exciting. As the frequency and amount of his play increased, Will began drawing on his retirement income and savings to continue to play. He now reports he lost money he needs for his university tuition while playing video games. His retirement check and G.I. Bill student stipend will arrive at the end of the month, but for now he feels worried about "scraping by" until the end of the month.

This client exhibits a number of strengths and weakness to consider in any treatment recommendation. The client is an older adult, without an extended social support system beyond his current continued attendance at meetings of Alcoholics Anonymous (AA). He lives alone and has few friends or acquaintances in Nevada. He has family in New England and widespread friends from the military, all of whom he contacts regularly via email. He reports prior history of a substance-related disorder, with successful sustained recovery following residential treatment. Will reports he is retired, receives adequate monthly retirement payments and tuition assistance payments, and usually lives well within his means.

Risk factors for this client include being an older adult, using nicotine, being relatively geographically and socially isolated, having a fixed income, and having ready access to gambling venues. Protective factors include having previous recovery experience, having relatively secure socioeconomic status, being in relatively good mental and physical health, and having sought information and assistance related to his emerging gambling behavior.

GPPC Dimensional Assessment

Dimension 1: Frequency/Intensity/Duration of Disorder   Current: 3 LOW

No current signs/symptoms of pathological gambling noted/reported. Client has not gambled for the last two weeks since he lost $1,100 over a two week period. Client began gambling approximately six months ago following retirement and relocation to Nevada. He usually gambles weekly, spending approximately $100 per episode, but recently began gambling more and more often. Client reports biggest one-day win of $500 and recent big loss of $1,100 while playing video poker. He reports recently losing money he needs for college tuition and living expenses. Client reports sporadic feelings of anxiety, guilt, and depression, as well as occasional sleep/appetite disturbance due to this loss. He denies current cravings or history of "chasing" behavior.

Dimension 2: Biomedical Conditions/Complications   Current: 2 LOW

Client describes his current overall physical condition as "good" and "stable," but "a little tired." He denies prior/current biomedical, dental, or communicable disease issues, but states he has not been to a doctor since his retirement physical two years ago. Client reports smoking up to one pack of cigarettes daily since 1968. He denies recent significant change in appetite/sleep patterns, change in weight, change in diurnal patterns of energy/mood, or recent change in sex drive. Currently his eyes/skin are clear, he appears alert and responsive, and he appears to be well-nourished and in relatively good physical condition. He reports he has not requested or required medical treatment recently and is not taking any medications. Client denies history of accident/injury or history of hospitalization other than tonsillectomy (age 6). Client has access to adequate health care services through local Veteran's Administration (VA) hospital.

Dimension 3: Cognitive/Behavioral/Emotional Conditions   Current: 2 LOW

Client reports prior diagnosis/treatment (1981, VAMC) for a substance-related disorder (303.90 Alcohol Dependence, With Physiological Dependence, In Sustained Full Remission). Client reports continuing abstinence and regular attendance at AA meetings locally. Client was raised by his biological parents and has three older siblings, all currently living in New England. Client denies family history of substance-related, mental health or behavioral disorders. Client reports no estrangement from family members. Client denies being the perpetrator or victim of verbal, emotional, physical, or sexual (VEPS) abuse or neglect as a child or adult. Client denies prior suicidal plan/attempt and denies family history of suicide/attempt. Client has never married and has no children. Client is retired, with regular retirement income, and has adequate housing. Client is a military veteran. Client has a high school diploma, a bachelor's degree, two master's degrees, and is a Ph.D. candidate at UNR. Client denies prior/current juvenile/adult criminal history or incarceration.

Dimension 4: Readiness to Change   Current: 1 LOW

Client sought assistance on his own initiative and appears to be sincere in his efforts to understand his gambling activities and change his behaviors. He appears to have strong internal motivation to change his thinking/behaviors and to sustain those changes. "I don't really understand my recent gambling episodes; I don't want to gamble like this again; it isn't fun anymore." He appears to be genuinely concerned about his long-term welfare and future. He is beginning to see the potentially harmful effects of problem gambling on emotional, physical, and mental health; potential legal and financial difficulties; and lingering effects on overall well-being. Based on his prior experience with AA, client requested referral information on local Gamblers Anonymous (GA) meetings. He appears to be in the Preparation stage of change based on interview and self-report.

Dimension 5: Relapse or Continued Problem History/Potentia   Current: 3 LOW

Client has only gambled, with relatively low frequency/intensity/duration, since arriving in Nevada six months ago. He has not gambled at all in the last two weeks and reports he is actively avoiding gaming venues. Based on his substance-related recovery experience, he is aware that gaming venues are "slippery" places, and he is exploring other recreational activities and social support in the area. He uses his understanding of relapse warning signs and triggers to "avoid problems before they become problems." Higher rating in this dimension reflects pervasive gaming activity in the local environment which contributes to somewhat greater relapse risk.

Dimension 6: Current Recovery/Living Environment   Current: 4 MODERATE

Client is unmarried, lives alone, and does not yet have an extended social support system beyond his contacts in AA. Client is initiating contacts with GA, his local church, and among fellow graduate students at UNR. Client has a regular, fixed income, adequate, safe housing, and adequate personal transportation. Client reports no current pressing educational, occupational, housing, economic, health care, legal, or other psychosocial or environmental problems. Higher rating in this dimension reflects relative isolation through age, social and housing circumstances.

Driving Dimensions: 1, 6

Client presents with relatively rapid-onset, binge-type gambling activity since arrival in Nevada (DIM 1). Client lives alone with little extended social support and lives on a fixed income (DIM 6). Client may lack prevention knowledge/skills/experience when dealing with gambling situations.

Suicidality; Threat to Self/Others: Current: 1 LOW

Client denies current SI/HI plan or intent. Current risk appears to be low (R1) based on no history of ideation, plan, or attempt. (A risk rating of R1 indicates the patient has adequate impulse control and coping skills to deal with any thoughts of harm to self or others.) Client reports strong internal inhibitors associated with his family, his religious beliefs, and his educational/career goals.

Vulnerabilities/Strengths:

Vulnerabilities: Client lives alone, on a fixed income, with little current social support in an intensively active gambling environment.

Strengths: Client has long-term recovery and relapse-prevention experience. Client appears to be willing to comply with treatment recommendations and appears to be concerned about his future with internal motivation for treatment. Client appears to be in relatively good physical and emotional health. Client appeared to be focused, responsive and cooperative throughout the interview.

Assessment Instruments Used and Results:

DSM-IV Diagnostic criteria for Pathological Gambling, lifetime: Client answered "Yes" to 1 of 10 items on this screening. (Answering "Yes" to one or two items on this instrument suggests the respondent is an "At-risk gambler." Answering "Yes" to three or four items suggests the respondent is a "Problem gambler." Answering "Yes" to 5 or more questions on this instrument meets diagnostic criteria for 312.31 Pathological Gambling); **GA 20 Questions**, lifetime: Client answered "Yes" to 3 of 20 items on this screening. ("Most compulsive gamblers will answer 'Yes' to at least seven of these questions"); **NODS**, lifetime: Client answered "Yes" to 1 of 17 items on this screening. (Answering "Yes" to 1 or 2 questions on this instrument indicates an "at-risk gambler." Answering "Yes" to 3 or 4 items on this instrument indicates a "problem gambler." Answering "Yes" to 5 to 10 items on this instrument indicates a "pathological gambler."); **SOGS**, lifetime: Client answered "Yes" to 3 of 20 items on this screening. (Answering "Yes" to 1-4 questions on this instrument indicates "some problems with gambling" Answering "Yes" to 5 or more items on this instrument indicates "probable pathological gambling.").

Clinical Impressions:

DSM-IV MULTIAXIAL ASSESSMENT

- Axis I: V71.09 No diagnosis on Axis I; prior Dx/Tx 303.90 Alcohol Dependence (With Physiological Dependence, In Sustained Full Remission) per client self-report; 305.1 Nicotine Dependence (With Physiological Dependence) per client self-report; rule out 296.00

- Axis II: V71.09 No diagnosis on Axis II

- Axis III: V71.09 No diagnosis on Axis III

- Axis IV: Primary support group; social environment; other psychosocial and environmental problems

- Axis V: 65 (current)

Client has experienced recent episodes of unsuccessful gambling outcomes which have produced transient cognitive and emotional upset. This client does not meet diagnostic criteria for 312.31 Pathological Gambling, based on assessment instrument results and clinical interview. Assessment instruments do indicate, however, that this client is an "at-risk gambler" with "some problems with gambling." Client appeared to be candid during the interview/assessment and appears to be aware of the unsuccessful nature of his recent thinking and behavior patterns. Client appears to believe early intervention will allow him to achieve and maintain more successful and prosocial behaviors. Client appears willing to initiate and comply with treatment.

As above, this client does present with early indications of potential pathological gambling. Client would clearly benefit from immediate Level 0.5 Brief Intervention Services emphasizing the biopsychosocial dimensions of problem gambling. As above, driving dimensions are Dimension 1 and Dimension 6, reflecting client's current acute episodes of problem gambling and client's current living environment, i.e., client lives alone in an intense gambling environment. Brief interventions should focus on Cognitive, Behavioral, and Emotional aspects of gambling to increase client awareness of risk/protective factors. Client also would benefit from psychoeducation concerning relapse prevention knowledge/skills and the protective influence of an extended stable social support system. Should client's acute behaviors/distress continue or worsen, however, transition to a higher level of care is indicated.

Reports Made; Consents Given:

At the client's request, and with signed release, a facsimile of this report was forwarded on 8/17/09 to the Clinical Director of the Renegade Gambling Treatment Center.

Provisional Treatment Plan & Discharge/Transition Criteria:

This client would benefit from GPPC Level 0.5 Brief Intervention Services, consisting of initial, individual psychoeducation and bibliotherapy (pamphlets, articles, workbooks, etc.) about gambling in general and the Impulse Control Disorder of Pathological Gambling, potential risk factors and protective factors, cognitive/behavioral techniques for regulating gambling behavior, warning signs and triggers for problem gambling, available treatment and recovery resources, and assistance with budgeting and financial planning. This client should be encouraged to begin seeking out additional social support and alternative recreational activities. As a university student, the client could be encouraged to seek out classes or seminars on addictive and impulse control disorders.

Prevention and early intervention approaches are appropriate for this client based on his history, current environment and behaviors. His recent experiences could serve as a timely "wake-up call" and protective interventions could avert accelerated gambling behaviors with associated negative consequences. Should the client's experiences and consequences become more severe, referral to GPPC Level One outpatient treatment and care is appropriate.

III
GPPC® Level 1.0 Outpatient Services

Vignette

A Typical GPPC Level One Outpatient Services Client

Daphne Doubledown is a 50-year-old, single White mother of two living in Las Vegas, Nevada. The client sought treatment after suffering significant negative consequences of long-term gambling. She reports regularly losing her paycheck during lengthy episodes of gambling from Friday payday through the weekend. Daphne reports having overdrawn her checking account multiple times and having exhausted all available financial resources. She is facing eviction from her apartment, repossession of her car, and has experienced significant behavioral problems with her children. Daphne reports regularly playing video gaming machines continuously throughout the weekend, with frequent episodes during the week when she feels "stressed," "depressed," or "wired."

Discussion

Problem Statement

Pathological gambling, an impulse control disorder, can develop gradually and may appear to be a relatively harmless social pastime. The problem gambler may initially rationalize the behavior while simultaneously begin to conceal or camouflage the excesses from others. Often, gamblers fully believe they will be able to reverse the negative consequences of their gambling problems through continued or accelerated gambling. As the gambler becomes more desperate, the behavior becomes less "invisible" to others. Behaviors, which had heretofore been largely ignored, overlooked or tolerated become more noticeable to others and the problem comes to a head as a result of some precipitating crisis, generally involving some sort of personal calamity with collateral damage. For example, a long-time, trusted employee may be found to have embezzled from his employer, lose his job, and face criminal charges. At the same time, the family may discover that savings and retirement accounts have been emptied, available credit resources have been overextended or exhausted, and home or car loans may be in default. The client and others begin to experience "clinically significant impairment or distress" as a result of the "persistent and recurrent maladaptive gambling behavior" included in the DSM-IV diagnostic criteria for pathological gambling.

Contributing Factors

Numerous biopsychosocial factors contribute to the risk and incidence of pathological gambling. Among these are age, gender, substance use, and co-occurring mental health disorders. Adolescents and older adults are at statistically higher risk of problem gambling behaviors and often have less financial resources to continue or recover from their behaviors. Men generally are "action gamblers," begin to gamble earlier than females and often have longer "gambling careers" before entering treatment. Women are generally "escape gamblers," begin to gamble later in life than males, and tend to enter treatment sooner than men. Gamblers in general are more likely to use tobacco and alcohol than non-gamblers. Gamblers generally report higher incidence of clinical or sub-clinical episodes of depression, anxiety, and/or bipolar disorder. For individuals with accessibility and susceptibility, these factors may be important "clues" or warning signs of potential problem gambling.

Intended Outcomes

Intended outcomes for this Level of Care (LOC) include arresting the client's problem behaviors, mediating the client's thinking errors, educating the client and significant others about the origins and consequences of problem gambling, referring the client to any additional social services or mental health services, teaching life skills, and educating the client on relapse prevention and recovery planning. Spouses or significant others are encouraged to participate in this level of care through attendance at family group sessions and participation in self-help, mutual support activities such as Gam-Anon, in that they constitute an important component of the client's recovery environment and support system.

Evidence-based Programs/Services

GPPC Level 1.0 (Level One or LOC I) care, from a biopsychosocial perspective, considers the client holistically, addressing the client's general medical health, mental health, and overall social functioning. The theoretical foundation for most Level One treatment is cognitive-behavioral therapy, addressing thinking and behavioral patterns which may have contributed to problem gambling, which may be impediments to treatment, and which may place the client at greater risk of relapse or recidivism post-treatment. Motivational interviewing, motivational enhancement, and solution-focused therapy are important components of treatment approaches at this level of care.

Services and Target Populations

GPPC Level One Outpatient (OP) Services provides structured treatment protocols for clients diagnosed with pathological gambling. This level of care is appropriate in a variety of settings and generally consists of evaluation, treatment, and recovery services. The intensity of services can be adjusted within the level of care dependent on the needs of the client. Minimum services at this level include one hour of individual services and/or one hour of group services per week. Based on the needs and circumstances of the client, Level One services can incorporate individual counseling, client case management, couple's counseling, family counseling, and group counseling, as needed. These services are provided in regularly scheduled sessions with a structured curriculum defined by provider or agency policies and procedures.

Particular treatment complications at Level One include clients with dual-diagnosis or co-occurring disorders; mandated, unmotivated, or non-compliant clients; or clients unwilling to commit to extended treatment commensurate with the severity of their disordered behavior. Clients at this level often struggle with impulsivity, compulsivity, and disordered thinking with regard to gambling behaviors. Techniques of benefit with these clients include determining where they may be in the progression of the disorder and where they may be in the Stages of Change continuum. Sharing this information with the client and significant others can mitigate the effects of underlying fears, misapprehensions, and misinformation. It is important that the client not be seen as the *object* of treatment, but rather a co-participant in treatment and recovery planning.

Evaluation

The best measure of effectiveness of a Level One program is a reduction or cessation of high-risk behaviors and negative consequences associated with gambling. Periodic re-administration of the GPPC (the "Review GPPC") may assist the clinician and client in evaluating progress toward achieving this goal. Significant regression or inability to attain/maintain progress may warrant transition to a higher level or intensity of care. Subjective descriptions of progress generally are expressed in terms of improved quality of life.

Agency Capacity

Employment of multiple individual, couples, family, and/or group services places higher demands on agency capacity. These demands extend from the logistics of space and scheduling of these sessions to the need for an appropriate number of properly credentialed counselors and supervisors for the caseload. Lack of adequate physical facilities and excessive caseloads diminish the quality and efficacy of treatment at this level of care.

Collaboration

Level One treatment will generally include referral from/to a variety of social services agencies, health professionals, and other treatment providers. These may include such things as child-care while the client attends treatment sessions, credit counseling, housing assistance, transportation, legal assistance, and spiritual support. Level One counselors must draw on the entire network of available services to be of optimum assistance to the client.

Summary

GPPC Level One intervention services provide a flexible approach to problem gambling treatment. It is appropriate for clients who remain able to function somewhat independently and autonomously despite their gambling problems. The program incorporates psychoeducation, individual and group counseling, couples/family counseling if needed, and referrals as needed for co-occurring disorders and other life concerns. Levels of care are adjustable as the needs/circumstances of the client change.

Case Study

Daphne Doubledown learned how to gamble literally at her grandfather's knee, seated on his lap during family card games on his farm in Iowa. She began to associate gambling with family, friendship, and a relaxing way to have a good time. Her parents hosted card parties in their home and children were encouraged to play at their own table. She was a "winner" early on, usually the best, most successful player. Eventually, playing for small stakes, Daphne was able to buy her own bicycle and was proud of her accomplishments.

Ms. Doubledown married directly after high school, moving with her husband to the California coast. She missed her family and friends, but began to build a large network of friends, again hosting card parties in her home. Her winnings allowed for "extras" and "treats" to supplement her husband's income, including special gifts and toys for her first child. She lavished attention on this daughter while her husband traveled for work.

Daphne's first marriage failed, largely due to the physical and emotional unavailability of her husband as well as several episodes of verbal, emotional and physical abuse fueled by his abuse of alcohol. She and her daughter returned to her mother's home in Iowa. She continued to join in family card games as a way to socialize and re-connect. Joining in these games gave her a sense of belonging.

Two years later, Daphne returned to California. "I missed the climate and lifestyle." She re-married within six months and had another child, a son. This husband, too, was often physically and emotionally unavailable. She again experienced verbal, emotional, and physical abuse by her husband when he was drinking. Daphne left this relationship within two years and moved to Las Vegas, Nevada, to "strike out on my own." She began working as a clerical assistant in a local bank; eventually becoming the Executive Secretary for the bank's managing vice president. She felt very proud of her accomplishments at work and as a successful single mother. She still wanted to play cards with friends and neighbors, but did not feel comfortable having card parties in her home with the children. She could not take her children into the casinos and did not feel she could afford additional child care if she went out in the evening without them.

Daphne soon noticed video poker machines at the supermarket. She was able to smoke cigarettes, "keep up" her poker skills, and keep an eye on her children all at the same time. She began to play for extended periods while her children waited. She had her first "big win" in a supermarket, over $1700, and was absolutely thrilled. She did, however, lose all her grocery money once and had to withdraw money from her savings to buy groceries that week. Daphne began to play video poker on the way to work while getting coffee at a convenience store and could play at a convenience store across from the bank at lunchtime or at casinos if she went out to lunch with co-workers. Poker as a table game became poker as a video game. She could play more, more often, and longer while still meeting all her obligations and responsibilities.

As her daughter got older, Daphne felt she could leave her children at home in the evening for a little while when she felt like going out to play video poker for "a few minutes." Sometimes she would get home quite late and find her daughter asleep on the sofa. As the children got older, they would sometimes leave the house alone when she was gone. She also started to get to work a few minutes late once or twice a week if she got a "really good hand" at the coffee shop on the way to work. Sometimes she was late back to work from lunch for the same reason. Daphne was so well-liked at work and such a capable employee that this behavior was easily overlooked or explained away. She always completed her work and prepared for the next day before leaving work each day.

As her gambling progressed, Daphne began spending more and more time and more and more money with each episode. She reduced, then eliminated, her regular savings and retirement account deductions in order to have more cash available to play. Soon she began drawing down those accounts, fully intending to replace and even increase these account balances. She eventually was reduced to living paycheck-to-paycheck even as she continued to get performance bonuses and raises. She moved to a smaller, cheaper apartment and traded in her car for an older, used car with smaller payments. She stopped buying new clothes and concentrated on only the necessities for her children and herself. She continued to gamble when "stressed, lonely, or bored." Daphne began to feel her losses reflected her being a "loser" as a person and parent, not just as a gambler.

Daphne felt she "hit bottom" within a one-week period. She had gambled almost continuously over the weekend (a long weekend), from Friday afternoon to Monday evening. She arrived at work Tuesday morning where she was confronted by her boss (the bank vice-president) about her increasing tardiness and absenteeism and repeated incidents of checks being returned for insufficient funds. The county District Attorney was considering prosecuting her for passing "bad" checks at numerous casinos in town. Her car was repossessed and she was evicted from her apartment that afternoon. She and her family stayed with a friend that evening. Daphne arranged to send her children to her mother's home the following weekend and attended her first Gamblers Anonymous meeting. There she met a co-worker who had been in GA for over ten years who arranged for a mutual friend to allow Daphne to sleep on a couch in the basement of her home as long as she attended daily GA meetings. Daphne got a sponsor the first week and attended her first GA "pressure relief group" to begin planning her financial restitution and recovery plan.

Daphne reports she has not placed a bet in the last 182 days. "It's been rough, but I get the support I need at GA. They know what I'm going through." She is still sleeping on her friend's couch, takes the bus to work, and goes straight to a meeting afterward. A fellow GA member meets with her weekly (on payday) to help her sort out and pay her bills. She calls her mother once a week and speaks to her children. "They're upset with me; angry and scared, but we're still talking."

Daphne denies prior/current medical, dental, or mental health problems and has not required/requested treatment recently. She has, however, voluntarily sought problem gambling counseling to augment the support she receives from GA. She is intent on getting as much help as she can for her gambling problem. She admits she has some "really dark days," but denies ever thinking about or planning suicide to resolve her problems.

GPPC Dimensional Assessment

Dimension 1: Frequency/Intensity/Duration of Disorder   **Current: 4 MODERATE**

No current signs/symptoms of pathological gambling noted/reported. Client has not gambled for the last six months since she lost $2100 over a two week period. Client began gambling at approximately age six and consequently has an almost-lifetime exposure to gambling and related activities. Client reports biggest one-day win of $500 and recent big loss of $1100 while playing video poker. Client gambled daily, spending up to $500 per episode. Client has been evicted from her home and has had her car repossessed. Client reports recurrent feelings of anxiety, guilt, and depression, as well as lingering sleep/appetite disturbance due to this loss and her current circumstances. Client denies current persistent or enduring cravings or urges to gamble.

Dimension 2: Biomedical Conditions/Complications   **Current: 3 LOW**

Client describes her current overall physical condition as "good" and "stable," but "a little tired and shaky sometimes." She denies prior/current biomedical, dental, or communicable disease issues, but states she has not been to a doctor for over a year. Client reports smoking up to one pack of cigarettes daily since age 18. She reports lingering appetite/sleep disturbance, but "not as bad as it used to be. I'm able to eat and sleep much better now." Currently her eyes/skin are clear, she appears alert and responsive, and she appears to be well-nourished and in relatively good physical condition. She reports she has not requested or required medical treatment recently. Client denies history of accident/injury or history of hospitalization other than tonsillectomy (age 6) and for the delivery of her two children. Client has access to adequate health care services through her employer's health benefits package.

Dimension 3: Cognitive/Behavioral/Emotional Conditions   **Current: 5 MODERATE**

Client denies prior/current treatment for mental/emotional problems. Client was raised by her biological parents, currently living in Iowa. Client reports no remarkable or long-term estrangement from immediate or extended family members. She has had to discipline her children for being out after curfew during some of her gambling episodes. Client denies history of verbal, emotional, physical, or sexual (VEPS) abuse or neglect as a child. She reports being the victim of verbal, emotional and physical abuse in her two marriages. This abuse was not reported. She denies child protective services (CPS) involvement with her children. Client denies prior/current suicidal plan/attempt and denies family history of suicide/attempt. Client has been married twice, is currently divorced, and has two children (son, age 15, daughter, age 19). Client is currently employed, but currently without personal transportation and is living in a friend's basement. Client is not a military veteran. Client has a high school diploma and an Associate's degree. Client denies prior/current juvenile/adult criminal history or incarceration, but reports she may face charges from the local district attorney concerning numerous checks for insufficient funds. She reports her thinking "gets really screwed up when I gamble." "I hate myself for doing this over and over and hurting my friends and family."

Dimension 4: Readiness to Change   **Current: 1 LOW**

Client sought assistance on her own initiative and appears to be sincere in her efforts to understand her gambling activities and change her behaviors. This positive attitude and high level of self-motivation presents a very low impediment to treatment. She appears to have strong internal and external motivation to change her thinking/behaviors and to sustain those changes. "I don't really understand how my gambling got so out of control; I don't want to gamble like this again; it isn't fun anymore." She appears to be genuinely concerned about her long-term welfare and future. She is beginning to see the reality of problem gambling and its harmful effects on emotional, physical, and mental health; significant legal and financial consequences; and pervasive effects on overall well-being. With the support of the self-help, mutual support she receives in GA, client believes she can be proactive in her recovery through seeking additional treatment. "I am *SO* ready; I want to build a new life." Client appears to be in the Preparation stage of change based on interview and self-report.

Dimension 5: Relapse or Continued Problem History/Potential   Current: 6 MODERATE

Client has a lifetime history of gambling and associated activities. She denies having gambled at all in the last six months and reports she is actively avoiding gaming venues. She is aware that gaming venues, to include convenience stores and supermarkets, are "slippery" places. She is exploring other recreational activities and social support in the area. She is becoming more aware of relapse warning signs and triggers in order to "avoid problems before they become problems." Higher rating in this dimension reflects pervasive gaming activity in the local environment which contributes to somewhat greater relapse risk.

Dimension 6: Current Recovery/Living Environment   Current: 6 LOW

Client is unmarried (divorced x2), lives in a friend's basement, and does not yet have an extended social support system of non-gamblers beyond her contacts in GA. Client is initiating extended social support contacts within GA as well as her local church. Client has employment income and has adequate, safe temporary housing. Client reports some pressing occupational, housing, transportation, legal, and other psychosocial or environmental concerns. Higher rating in this dimension reflects relative isolation through age, social, occupational, transportation, legal and housing circumstances.

Driving Dimensions: 1, 3, 5, 6

Client presents with long-term, persistent and pervasive gambling and associated behaviors (DIM 1). Client reports distress at her behaviors and significant negative self-esteem (DIM 3). Client lacks independent relapse prevention knowledge/skills/experience or long-term recovery strategies (DIM 5). Client lives with friends temporarily with little extended social support (DIM 6).

Suicidality; Threat to Self/Others: Current: 1 LOW

Client denies current SI/HI plan or intent. Current risk appears to be low (R1) based on no history of ideation, plan, or attempt. (A risk rating of R1 indicates the patient has adequate impulse control and coping skills to deal with any thoughts of harm to self or others.) Client reports strong internal inhibitors associated with her family and her religious/spiritual values.

Vulnerabilities/Strengths:

Vulnerabilities: Client is staying temporarily with friends, but basically lives alone, with little current extended social support in an intensively active gambling environment. Client has no personal transportation and is facing potential legal action.

Strengths: Client appears to be willing to comply with GA and treatment recommendations and appears to be concerned about her current/future with internal/external motivation for treatment. Client appears to be in relatively good physical and emotional health. Client appeared to be focused, responsive, and cooperative throughout the interview.

Assessment Instruments Used and Results:

DSM-IV diagnostic criteria for Pathological Gambling, lifetime: 7/10 "Yes" (Answering "Yes" to 5 or more questions on this instrument meets diagnostic criteria for 312.31 Pathological Gambling); **GA 20 Questions**, lifetime: 16/20 "Yes" ("Most compulsive gamblers will answer 'Yes' to at least seven of these questions"); **NODS**, lifetime: 10/17 "Yes" (Answering "Yes" to 5 or more questions on this instrument indicates a "pathological gambler"); **SOGS**, lifetime: 13/20 "Yes" (Answering "Yes" to 5 or more questions on this instrument indicates "probable pathological gambling").

Clinical Impressions:

DSM-IV MULTIAXIAL ASSESSMENT

- Axis I: 312.31 Pathological Gambling; 305.1 Nicotine Dependence (with Physiological Dependence) per client self-report; rule out 296.00
- Axis II: V71.09 No diagnosis on Axis II
- Axis III: V71.09 No diagnosis on Axis III
- Axis IV: Primary support group; social environment; housing; transportation; occupation; legal; other psychosocial and other environmental problems
- Axis V: 61 (current)

This client meets diagnostic criteria for 312.31 Pathological Gambling, based on assessment instrument results and clinical interview, and as evidenced by: preoccupation with gambling; the need to gamble with increasing amounts of money in order to achieve the desired excitement; repeated unsuccessful efforts to control, cut back, or stop gambling; restlessness or irritability when attempting to cut down or stop gambling; gambling as a way of escaping from problems or of relieving dysphoric mood; lying to others to conceal the extent of involvement with gambling; and reliance on others to provide money to relieve a desperate financial situation caused by gambling. Client has experienced recurrent episodes of unsuccessful, unsatisfactory gambling outcomes which have produced significant cognitive and emotional upset, impairment and distress. Client appeared to be candid during the interview/assessment and appears to be aware of the unsuccessful nature of her recent thinking and behavior patterns. Client appears to believe treatment intervention will allow her to achieve and maintain successful and prosocial behaviors, improved quality of life, and reduced threats to personal and family wellness. Client appears willing to initiate and comply with treatment.

As above, this client does present with pathological gambling. Client would clearly benefit from immediate GPPC Level One Outpatient Services emphasizing the biopsychosocial dimensions of disordered gambling. As above, driving dimensions are 1, 3, 5 and 6, reflecting client's history of disordered gambling, client's emotional distress, client's lack of relapse prevention knowledge/skills/experience, and client's current living environment. Outpatient treatment interventions should focus on Cognitive, Behavioral, and Emotional aspects of gambling to increase client awareness of risk/protective factors. Client also would benefit from psychoeducation concerning relapse prevention knowledge/skills and the protective influence of an extended stable support system. Should client's acute behaviors/distress continue or worsen, or should the client relapse during treatment, however, transition to a higher level of care is indicated.

Reports Made; Consents Given:

At the client's request, and with signed release, a facsimile of this report was forwarded on 8/17/09 to the Clinical Director of the Renegade Gambling Treatment Center in Las Vegas, the client's attorney, and the office of the Clark County District Attorney.

Provisional Treatment Plan & Discharge/Transition Criteria:

This client would benefit from GPPC Level One Outpatient Services, consisting of initial, individual psychoeducation and bibliotherapy about gambling in general and the nature of disordered gambling, potential risk factors and protective factors, cognitive/behavioral techniques for regulating gambling behavior, warning signs and triggers for disordered gambling, available treatment and recovery resources, and assistance with budgeting and financial planning. This client should be encouraged to begin seeking out additional social support and alternative recreational activities.

Outpatient intervention approaches are appropriate for this client based on her gambling history, emotional distress, relapse potential and current living environment. Outpatient services would allow the client to maintain her employment and actively engage in recommended GA 12-Step, self-help, mutual support. Intervention at this time could avert accelerated gambling behaviors with associated increasingly severe negative consequences. Should the client's experiences and consequences become more severe, referral to GPPC Level Two Intensive Outpatient (IOP) treatment and care is appropriate.

Disposition/Follow-Up/Appointment/Re-interview:

Client has agreed to begin Level One treatment on 8/24/09 at 9:30 a.m. at the Renegade Gambling Treatment Center and to continue GA meetings three times per week. Client agrees to periodic review/re-evaluation using the GPPC until all dimensions are rated "Low" at which time she will transition to Continuing Care for up to one year.

Referrals:

Client requested, and was provided with, referral information concerning parenting skills, financial management and credit counseling.

IV
GPPC® Level 2.0
Intensive Outpatient Services

Vignette

A Typical GPPC Level 2.0 Intensive Outpatient Services Client

Izzy Goingtobet is a 59-year-old married White male. He sought help from his EAP counselor for his gambling problem, but felt that it was wasted time as it did not give him the help he felt he urgently needed. He sought out other more intensive treatment on his own. His stated reasons for seeking counseling include his inability to stop gambling, "chasing" his losses, marital difficulties and his increasing credit card debt. He is currently $140,000 in debt. He used his credit cards to finance his gambling and has no disposable income even though he is gainfully employed. He has a 40-year history of gambling and his gambling has been out of control since moving to Reno six years ago. Until last week he was gambling on a daily basis and the amounts of his bets were increasing. He gambles $500-$1000 each session. His problematic gambling has created serious problems in his marriage; he reports his wife is thinking of a separation. His gambling has created many financial problems. He can no longer make his monthly credit card payments and is having a hard time making the mortgage payments. His gambling has affected both his physical and mental health. At the present time, gambling exacerbates his blood pressure and he feels anxious and depressed.

Discussion

A GPPC Level 2.0 Intensive Outpatient (IOP) Services program offers multi-modal, educational, individual, family and group counseling to problem gamblers, while providing strategies to stop or reduce their destructive and dysfunctional gambling behaviors. IOP services can improve clients' life circumstances by helping to develop healthier thinking patterns that encourage abstinence from gambling.

The Level 2.0 (Level Two or Level II) program is a minimum of six weeks duration, with clients meeting for two hours per day, four times per week. Clients attend individual, process group and family group sessions. Concurrent attendance at Gamblers Anonymous (GA) meetings is strongly encouraged during intensive outpatient treatment. IOP group sessions are offered in both day and evening sessions to accommodate clients with different work schedules. Clients are encouraged to continue regular therapeutic sessions at reduced frequency and intensity for up to six months after they complete the initial six-week Level Two program and commit to weekly Continuing Care sessions for up to one year thereafter. An IOP program is flexible and diverse in its frequency, intensity and duration of services to better respond to the chronicity and severity of compulsive gambling and other problems.

The primary advantages at this level of care are the considerable opportunities for daily interaction within the treatment program and the different realities presented by each client on a daily basis. Clients come to treatment in crisis from the damage of their destructive gambling behaviors. They are confronted with the individual, family, social and financial stresses and consequences of their present circumstances while continually facing the inevitable gambling cues and triggers. The ongoing events of their daily lives can be examined and dealt with by the group process and can be used as the basis for life skills training, improved communication skills, listening skills, refusal skills, and problem-solving skills. Clients learn how to manage urges and negative thinking, plan for emergencies and practice relapse prevention. The program provides an opportunity to discuss and practice skills with other clients in similar situations. A Level Two program can meet the need for ongoing support as the clients struggle to deal with problems in their lives caused by their destructive gambling behaviors. They can confront the harm done to themselves and their families. The IOP program allows clients opportunities to deal with urges to gamble in a supportive, constructive environment. In the event of a slip or relapse, the Level Two program allows for early intervention in the relapse recovery process and adjustment in treatment as needed.

Problem Statement

GPPC Level Two IOP treatment is indicated for clients who have progressed, or are actively progressing, from prodromal problem gambling to pathological gambling. These clients are generally physically and emotionally stable, are capable of an autonomous level of functioning, and can function effectively in individual, group and/or family therapy environments. This level of care is appropriate for clients in crisis who require structured, multi-modal (biopsychosocial) treatment involving educational and process groups as well as individual, group and family therapy. IOP programs incorporate case management, crisis intervention and the support of other related mental health and social services. Many IOP programs strongly encourage the inclusion of Gamblers Anonymous 12-Step, self-help/mutual-support group meetings as part of the program to alleviate the impact of years of compulsive gambling and to improve the client's level of functioning on the individual, family and social level.

Contributing Factors

Factors contributing to the need for IOP treatment generally are reflective of the progressive nature of problem gambling. Generally the client is experiencing increased frequency, intensity and duration of problematic gambling behaviors with increasingly severe individual, family, social, financial and/or legal consequences. Often there has been some precipitating crisis which has exposed the formerly suppressed signs and symptoms of pathological gambling. The client's perceived need for help is more urgent and the potential consequences of the disordered behavior are more severe. IOP offers a safe, stable and structured environment, as often as daily, for the client to recuperate and plan for a healthier future.

Intended Outcomes

The goals of Level II IOP treatment focus on fostering cognitive and behavioral changes that support abstinence from gambling and a new way of living. An IOP program facilitates active participation in community-based support systems, assists clients in identifying and addressing a wide range of psychosocial problems, and improves clients' problem-solving skills and coping strategies. IOP programs help the client change problematic behaviors by identifying and addressing the causes of problem gambling, improving emotional functioning, facilitating a 12-Step self-help/mutual-support system, and creating and implementing a relapse prevention and continuing care plan.

Evidence-based Programs/ Services

Evidence-based counseling modalities, techniques and strategies used in counseling are those that have been evaluated scientifically to support their use in treatment. They are classified according to the scientific evidence supporting their efficacy. Generally, evidence-based approaches are classified as having strong evidence, moderate evidence or weak evidence supporting their use and effectiveness in treatment and the empirical rigor used in their evaluation.

Cognitive Behavioral Therapy appears to be the most empirically supported treatment approach for pathological gambling, i.e., there is strong evidence supporting use of this treatment protocol. This approach includes Cognitive Restructuring, Problem Solving training, and Social and Coping Skills training.

Several behavioral approaches also appear to be effective, including Aversion/Avoidance therapy and Desensitization. A number of behavioral therapeutic techniques also show strong evidence basis. These include: Aversion therapy, stimulus-control and cue-exposure with response prevention, systematic desensitization, and self-exclusion or avoidance techniques.

Some accepted interventions, while showing weaker evidence basis, are appropriate for a Level II IOP program. These include relapse prevention and recovery training, various 12-Step self-help and mutual-support programs (such as Gamblers Anonymous), Psychodynamic therapy, Solution-focused brief therapy, and Motivational Enhancement. These interventions can be augmented with financial counseling and credit management training, life skills training, psychopharmacological intervention, smoking cessation, meditation and journaling techniques.

Services and Target Populations

Level II IOP programs draw on numerous components of other levels of care. These include continuing biopsychosocial assessment/evaluation using the GPPC and referral for treatment of co-occurring disorders. During the Level II IOP phase, the treatment plan can be adjusted, based on the client's needs, with regard to transition to Level III or Level I treatment. Near the conclusion of Level II, the treatment team focuses on transition to continuing care or discharge planning. Typically, Level II clients will have higher ratings within and between GPPC dimensions compared to Level I clients. Often, Level II clients are experiencing more significant impairment or distress. Many Level II clients are also experiencing co-occurring or concurrent disorders. IOP treatment is generally indicated for clients in crisis who require structured, multi-modal (bio-psychosocial) treatment involving educational and process groups as well as individual, group and family therapy. IOP incorporates case management, crisis intervention and the support of other related mental health and social services.

Evaluation

Evaluation of client progress in Level Two treatment, based on presentation at intake, occurs periodically during treatment, and at transition/discharge using the GPPC. Significant changes in one or more dimensions may suggest a change in Level of Care or intensity of treatment.

Agency Capacity

Determining factors for agency capacity to provide Level Two IOP treatment include the number of trained counselors on staff and the physical size of the facility itself. The recommended size for Level Two process groups is up to 12 members. Agencies should consider using a waiting-list or opening an additional group when the group census exceeds 12. The agency should be prepared for clients who stay longer than six weeks, for clients working rotating or variable work shifts, and should recognize that individual clients progress at different rates. Clients must be assured that they can remain in treatment as long as they feel the need and that the agency can adequately respond to those needs.

Collaboration

Collaboration should be open and reciprocal, and can include making referrals and accepting referrals from various social service, private practice, legal, financial and mental health organizations. Level Two counselors must draw on the entire network of available social and health services to be of optimum assistance to the client.

Case Study

Izzy Goingtobet is 59-year-old married White male self-referred to evaluation, counseling and treatment after seeking help through his EAP counselor. He has worked for the same technology company for many years and is in upper management. Izzy stated his reason for seeking help at this time is "I need help stopping gambling, it is killing me, I need to change." "I owe $140,000 in credit card bills, I have no money now and my wife has found out." "I was able to stay sober for 14 years, but now I know I can't stop gambling by myself; I know I have a problem." He last gambled one week ago and reports that at present he is very impatient, irritable and agitated, depressed, has anxiety and headaches, and cannot eat or sleep. Izzy states he is experiencing cravings to gamble, is preoccupied with going back and winning and is very tense. He has a 40-year history of gambling. Izzy originally started gambling in college: "I continued gambling on and off like everybody else throughout my life. It really became serious about six years ago when I moved to Reno."

His problematic gambling has created serious problems in his marriage, caused social isolation and threatened his interpersonal relationships. His gambling has affected him financially; his wife has told him she thinks he is stealing from her. "She wants me to get help for myself and fix myself." He has knowingly written checks with insufficient funds, manipulated financial accounts, and maxed out all credit cards. He is now getting daily calls from credit card companies because he cannot meet the payments. He progressed to gambling on a daily basis. Izzy started gambling playing poker, betting on office pools and, when he moved to Reno, started playing blackjack. Now his game of choice is video poker. When he gambles, he plays anywhere from $500 to $1000 each session. The longest amount of time he has been able to stop gambling has been three weeks. His biggest win was $5100 in 2005 and his biggest loss was $2200 last year. "My gambling has affected everything, my self-worth, financially I'm broke, my wife is ready to leave, my honesty, my job, you name it."

Izzy describes his physical health as, "okay, stable." He does have back and knee problems, has had surgeries on both, but is not currently on any medication for these conditions. He has allergies and takes medications for them with satisfactory result. He also takes high blood pressure medication and reports that his blood pressure is erratic and often exacerbated by his gambling activities. He has no dental issues, reports no changes in appetite or weight, but does report changes in his mood, sleep and energy patterns. He has no prior/current suicidal ideation, plans or attempts. He received three DUIs in the 1980s and this was the catalyst to stop his drinking. He also worked a self-help, 12-Step program through AA and his sponsor. He attended six years of college but did not receive a degree. He has a prior work history as a juvenile social worker. He served three years in the Army in Viet Nam. He has seen a counselor a couple of times in the past on a weekly basis for six months and he attended alcohol counseling when he was in his forties. He also attended counseling after returning from Viet Nam. He has always been bothered by his war experiences. He has attended three GA meetings recently. He has not had previous gambling treatment.

Both of his parents are deceased: his father was an alcoholic and a pathological gambler; his mother had no addiction issues, but she enabled Izzy's father by always bailing him out. Izzy is an only child. He denies issues of sexual abuse but reports that he did suffer verbal, emotional and physical abuse from his alcoholic father. "My mother was the one who suffered from his abusiveness." He did not get married until he was forty-two and has been married to his current wife for fifteen years. She has three children and he considers them as his own. He is the only one in the family who gambles. He has few friends except for his wife and their family. He has no current or prior mental health diagnosis or disorder. His daily stressors are, "not being able to stop gambling, credit card bills, no money, the anger and mistrust of my wife (she is talking about a separation), disliking myself and not learning from my alcohol and drug problems." He has abused methamphetamines heavily and was arrested for possession, served time and stopped using drugs in his thirties. He has more than adequate housing ("a great house") and he and his wife make a good living. They are both professionals. They both have adequate transportation and "most everything" they need. "I want to stop gambling and enjoy my life; I don't want to lose my wife."

Izzy describes change as being hard for him, but knows he is capable of changing because he stopped drinking for 14 years and stopped using drugs for over 30 years. His mood and affect are congruent and appropriate. He seems sincere in his desire to change. He is aware of the harmful effects and negative consequences his gambling has caused. His triggers to gamble are, "having access to money, credit, phone calls from creditors, facing the bills and escaping from my mistakes." The best thing about stopping gambling would be, "getting my life back and finding myself and fixing my marriage." He completed all necessary paperwork on his own and states he will go along with, and wants to complete, a treatment program.

His screening instrument answers are: 6/10 "yes" on the DSM-IV Screen for Pathological Gambling, 13/20 "yes" on the Gamblers Anonymous 20 questions, 11/17 "yes" on the NORC DSM-IV Screen (NODS), and 13/20 "yes" on the SOGS.

GPPC Dimensional Assessment

<u>Dimension 1: Frequency/Intensity/Duration of Disorder</u>   **<u>Current: 7 HIGH</u>**

    Mr. Goingtobet sought help on his own after consulting his EAP at work. "I need help to stop gambling; it is killing me; I need to change." He has no money and his wife recently found out about the huge credit card advances used to finance his gambling. He reports current symptoms of impatience, agitation, restlessness, depression and anxiety, sleep disturbances, headaches, eating problems, cravings and preoccupation. He reports a forty-year history of gambling. The past six years it has been "out of control." This has caused serious marital (wife wanting separation), social, financial and interpersonal difficulties. He is under pressure from his wife and credit card companies, who are calling daily. He reports the most recent gambling episode was one week ago. He started gambling playing poker and betting in office pools. When he moved to Reno, he started playing blackjack; now his game of choice is video poker. He routinely gambles daily, up to $500-$1,000 each session. He reports his biggest one-time win was $5100 in 2005 and his biggest one-time loss was $2200 last year. He reports co-occurring substance-related disorders currently in remission. He smokes a pack of cigarettes each day. He states that he has been sober/abstinent from alcohol for 14 years. He also reports that he abused methamphetamines heavily in the past and was arrested for possession, served time in jail, and stopped using drugs in his thirties.

<u>Dimension 2: Biomedical Conditions/Complications</u>   **<u>Current: 3 LOW</u>**

    Client describes his physical health as, "okay, stable." He reports that he does have back and knee problems, has had surgeries for both, but is not currently on any medication for these problems. He reports that he has allergies and takes medications for them with satisfactory results. He smokes up to one pack of cigarettes daily. He also takes high blood pressure medication. He reports his blood pressure is erratic and that gambling exacerbates his blood pressure. He has no dental issues, denies changes in appetite or weight, but does report changes in his mood, sleep and energy. He reports that there are no medical issues that would be prevent him from attending or completing treatment.

<u>Dimension 3: Cognitive/Behavioral/Emotional Conditions</u>   **<u>Current: 5 MODERATE</u>**

    Client denies current or prior mental health diagnosis or disorder. He is not taking any medications for mental health issues. Both of his parents are deceased. His father was an alcoholic and a pathological gambler; his mother had no addiction issues, but she enabled Izzy's father by always bailing him out. He is an only child. He denies issues of sexual abuse, but reports he did suffer verbal, emotional and physical abuse from his alcoholic father. He reports his mother also suffered emotional and verbal abuse from his father. He reports that he is distressed and has anxiety over his wife talking about separation. He reports that he abused methamphetamines heavily and was arrested for possession, served time in jail, and stopped using drugs in his thirties. He reports that he has knowingly written checks with insufficient funds, has manipulated financial accounts and has maxed out all credit cards. He reports seeing a counselor a couple of times in the past on a weekly basis for six months. He previously attended alcohol counseling in his forties. He reports serving three years active duty in Viet Nam and attended counseling after returning from Viet Nam. Izzy's counselor treated him for symptoms of PTSD. He reports no current or prior suicidal ideation, plans or attempts. He appears to be at low risk for suicide or harming others. He reports his daily stressors are not being able to stop gambling, credit card bills, no money, the anger and mistrust of his wife (she is talking about a separation), disliking himself and not learning from his alcohol and drug problems.

Dimension 4: Readiness for Change   Current: 2 LOW

The client appears to be both internally and externally motivated to change his behaviors ("I want to stop gambling and enjoy my life and I don't want to lose my wife"). He is trying to save his marriage because his wife is talking of separation. His mood is appropriate when talking about his desire to stop gambling. His affect is congruent and he seems sincere in his desire to change even though change is hard for him. He is aware of the harmful effects and negative consequences his gambling has caused. He reports the best thing about stopping gambling would be, "getting my life back and finding myself." He reports that the longest amount of time he has been able to stop gambling has been three weeks. He reports that he has attended three Gamblers Anonymous meetings recently. He appears to be in the Preparation Stage of Change based on self-report. ("I know I can't stop gambling by myself, I know I have a problem.")

Dimension 5: Relapse or Continued Problem History/Potential   Current: 7 HIGH

Mr. Goingtobet has a 40-year history of gambling. He originally started gambling in college ("I continued gambling on and off like everybody else throughout my life and it really became serious about six years ago when I moved to Reno"). He started gambling playing poker, betting in office pools, and, when he moved to Reno, started playing blackjack. His game of choice is now video poker. He reports that he really wants to stop gambling ("I was able to stay sober for 14 years, but now I know I can't stop gambling by myself. I know I have a problem"). He has remained sober through Alcoholics Anonymous, working the 12 Steps and having a sponsor. He has been alcohol-free for 14 years and drug-free for 30 years. He is overdrawn on his checking account and he reports being preoccupied with thoughts of gambling, recouping his losses and making money to pay his bills. He has increased tolerance for his betting patterns and numerous failed attempts to stop gambling. He reports his triggers to gamble are, "having access to money, credit, phone calls from creditors, facing the bills and escaping from my mistakes." He reports the best thing about stopping gambling would be, "getting my life back and finding myself and fixing my marriage." He reports that he has no prior gambling treatment. He does have some effective relapse prevention knowledge, experience and skill related to his continued sobriety, but remains very vulnerable to relapse to gambling. He would benefit from continued relapse prevention skills training included in gambling treatment.

Dimension 6: Current Recovery/ Living Environment   Current: 5 MODERATE

Client reports more than adequate housing. He and his wife make a good living; both are professionals. They both have adequate transportation and "everything" they need. He does have support from his spouse, ("She wants me to get help for myself and fix myself"). He also has the support of his family, but these relationships have been strained by his gambling behaviors. His family will likely contribute positively to his recovery. He reports few friends and has little social support. He reports no legal issues at this time. There are no family members who gamble. He is currently employed and has a very good job.

Driving Dimensions: 1,3.5,6

GPPC Dimensions 1, 3, 5 and 6 are the driving dimensions based on frequency, intensity, and duration of his gambling, his addiction history, and his current symptoms and level of functioning. His cognitive/behavioral history and emotional volatility will be factors and influences in his recovery. His high potential for relapse, lack of relapse prevention skills and knowledge in terms of gambling and lack of extended stable social support system will also influence his recovery. Based on the intensity, duration and severity of Dimensions 1, 3, 5 and 6, this client would benefit from GPPC Level II Intensive Outpatient treatment and care for pathological gambling.

Suicidality/Threat to Self/Others: Current: 1 LOW

Client denies prior or current suicidal ideation, has never attempted suicide and has never reported violence. He appears to be a low risk of harm himself or others. Current risk appears to be low (R0), based on no history of ideation, plan or attempt. (A risk rating of R0 indicates the patient has good impulse control and coping skills.) He reports inhibitors to suicidality being his respect for life and the love of his wife, children and granddaughter.

Vulnerabilities/Strengths:

The client's strengths appear to be his motivation to get help, seeking counseling, wanting to change his behavior, and wanting to repair his marriage. He has 14 years of sobriety, the support of his family, knowledge of the counseling process, lack of legal issues, stable employment, knowledge of a 12-Step program and willingness to commit to an intensive outpatient program.

His vulnerabilities are the intensity, duration and frequency of his gambling, family of origin addiction issues, being overwhelmed with debts, his wife's anger and mistrust, lack of a social support system and his high relapse potential.

Assessment Instruments Used and Results:

Client answered "Yes" to 6/10 questions on the **DSM-IV Diagnostic Criteria** (5 or more "Yes" answers on this screening meets diagnostic criteria for 312.31 Pathological Gambling.) He answered "Yes" to 13/20 questions on the **Gamblers Anonymous 20 Questions** (7 or more "Yes" answers on this survey suggests probable Compulsive Gambling.) He answered "Yes" to 11/17 questions on the **NORC DSM-IV Screen for Gambling Problem (NODS)** instrument (5 or more "Yes" answers on this screening indicates a "pathological gambler.") He answered "Yes" to 13/20 questions on **South Oaks Gambling Screen (SOGS)** instrument (5 or more "Yes" answers on this instrument indicates "probable pathological gambling.") All assessment scores support the diagnosis of 312.31 Pathological Gambling.

Clinical Impressions:

This client meets diagnostic criteria for 312.31 Pathological Gambling, as evidenced by maladaptive gambling behavior including: preoccupation with gambling; need to gamble with increasing amounts; repeated unsuccessful efforts to control, cut back, or stop gambling; restlessness/irritability when attempting to cut down/stop gambling; after losing, "chasing" losses; lying to others to conceal extent of involvement with gambling. Based on the frequency, intensity and duration of the disorder and the severity of Dimensions One, Three, Five and Six, this client would benefit from GPPC Level II Intensive Outpatient treatment and care, with an emphasis on treatment of pathological gambling.

His mood, affect, speech, behaviors and ability to focus during the interview are all congruent and appropriate. He appears to be in the Preparation Stage of Change. He appeared to be candid, and aware of the unsuccessful nature of his thinking and behavior patterns. He believes he can complete the program as well as sustain and, with help, maintain abstinence from gambling.

DSM-IV MULTIAXIAL ASSESSMENT

- Axis I: 312.31 Pathological Gambling

  303.90 Alcohol Dependence (Sustained Full Remission) per client self-report

  304.40 Amphetamine Dependence (Sustained Full Remission) per client self-report

  305.1 Nicotine Dependence per client self-report

- Axis II: V71.09 No Diagnosis
- Axis III: 401.9 Hypertension per client self-report
- Axis IV: Problems with primary support group, economic problems, other psychosocial problems
- Axis V: GAF=65 (Current)

Reports Made; Consents Given:

All release forms and consents are signed and with the client's permission a copy will be forwarded to the Clinical Director of the Reno Problem Gambling Center.

Provisional Treatment Plan and Discharge/Transition Criteria:

Based on DSM-IV diagnosis of 312.31 Pathological Gambling, clinical interview and other assessment tools indicating compulsive gambling, the client's work schedule, his self-report, his willingness to attend treatment, and his being in the Preparation Stage of Change, it is recommended that the client begin Intensive Outpatient treatment immediately at the Reno Problem Gambling Center. The client agrees to attend daily groups (Monday-Thursday) from 9:30-11:30 AM and Family Group on Tuesday evening from 6:00-8:30 PM for a minimum of six weeks or until treatment goals are met. He agrees to start next Monday. The focus will be on cognitive and behavioral changes and on relapse prevention. It is also recommended that he attend three GA meetings per week while in IOP treatment. He is aware that upon successful completion of the above outlined program he should also seek out additional social support and recreational activities, continue to attend continuing care groups, and continue attending GA meetings.

V
GPPC® Level 3.0
Residential Treatment Services

Vignette

A Typical GPPC Level 3.0 Residential Treatment Services Client

Kay Syrah is a widowed, 62-year-old White female, who quit her job and took early retirement (Social Security Benefits—her only income) in order to pursue her true love, gambling. She had become so preoccupied with gambling that her productivity at work had dropped to a new low. Kay felt that since she could not think of anything but gambling, she could make it her full-time job.

Kay began gambling five years ago after the unexpected death of her husband of 30 years. In order to fill the emptiness in her life, Kay began going to casinos. The bright lights and din of the multitudes provided her with "friends." She started out playing penny slots, a penny at a time. She became so enamored by the game her playing quickly escalated to five dollars per bet, to $25 per bet, to $100 per bet. She needed to bet with increased amounts of money to continue to feel the high of being in action. However, her winning streak soon ended and Kay mortgaged her home, eventually losing it to foreclosure, in order to pursue her gambling career. She then took a title loan on her car because she knew she was "due" for a big win; after all she lost her home and the casino "owed" it to her.

Upon the loss of her car Kay became very depressed. Both of her parents are deceased and her children no longer speak to her because she gambled away their inheritance. She has no more friends since she isolated herself in the casino and lost contact with them because all of her time was spent gambling. The one friend she did maintain contact with soon quit speaking to her upon discovering Kay had stolen jewelry from her and pawned it. Kay found herself homeless and penniless. She became irritable, angry, and anxious. She developed gastrointestinal problems and began swallowing antacids like candy. In addition, she developed high blood pressure. She could not concentrate enough to pursue a job—besides gambling was her job, and it would soon pay off. She states she would rather die than live in a homeless shelter, and she began thinking of ways to achieve this goal.

Discussion

Problem Statement

Problem gambling is a progressive mental health disorder in which an individual has a psychological preoccupation with gambling and the urge to gamble. This can result in excessive gambling, the outcome of which is loss of time, money and self-esteem. The gambling can progress to a point at which it compromises, disrupts, and ultimately destroys the gambler's personal life, family relationships and vocational pursuits (Nevada Council on Problem Gambling, 2005).

As individuals progress through the continuum of gambling behavior (from no gambling through pathological gambling), they can become so preoccupied with gambling that it affects all areas of their lives, often to the extent they are no longer able to participate in the basic activities of daily living. They no longer control the gambling, the gambling controls them. These persons, because of specific functional deficits, need a safe, stable environment wherein they can learn the tools to become gambling free and enjoy the incredible journey of recovery.

Contributing Factors

Various forms of gambling are legal in all but two of our 50 states, Hawaii and Utah. Even in those two states there is illegal gambling. Potential gamblers in Hawaii can access special air trips that bring planeloads of gamblers to the mainland to gamble; potential gamblers in Utah can drive to adjacent states, notably Nevada, to gamble. Internet and offshore gambling are becoming prevalent. Sports betting has always been popular. Add the prevalence of alcohol use, cigarette smoking and the use of other drugs to the mix and gambling becomes another player in the serotonergic, noradrenergic, and dopaminergic triad of disordered behavior.

Intended Outcomes

The intended outcomes for a GPPC Level of Care III (LOC III) are to reduce the gambler's depression, anxiety and stress to the point they can concentrate on learning coping strategies and the tools to get and remain gambling free. Cleaning up and rebuilding the client's financial situation is a primary goal. A gambler's credit pressures, personal debt and property loss are often the stimuli for suicidal thoughts and attempts. Gamblers can reduce the hopelessness and helplessness they feel through treatment, thus reducing the risk and incidence of suicide.

Preoccupation with gambling, so prevalent in the pathological gambler, contributes greatly to lost productivity and absenteeism in the workplace. Improving productivity and reducing absenteeism is an important outcome of residential treatment. Another intended outcome is to reduce the economic, legal, and social effects of bad checks, embezzlement, robbery, and insurance fraud when the gambler reaches the Desperation Phase of gambling. (See Dr. Robert L. Custer's "V-chart" of compulsive gambling and recovery, in the Chart Module, for more information on progressive phases of gambling and recovery for both the problem gambler and affected significant other.) The goal of residential treatment is to offer other, more productive options to the client to prevent them from falling into the Hopelessness Phase and moving directly into the Critical Phase. However, a client does not need to be in the Desperation Phase to be admitted into residential treatment.

The intended outcome of LOC III residential treatment is to decrease losses of contributions by citizens; reduce embezzlement, forgery, and tampering of bank records; reduce bankruptcy and the collapse of business and investment, reduce the failure to pay taxes, rent, and other financial obligations; reduce employee absenteeism; and lower the costs of trials and incarcerations which are currently borne by family, friends and the community. More importantly, one hopes that residential treatment is only the beginning of the road to recovery. Level of Care II Intensive Outpatient treatment or continuing care is highly encouraged upon discharge from residential treatment. If the client's family or occupational priorities preclude intensive outpatient, a Level I Outpatient treatment program is recommended. Beyond all of the above potential outcomes, residential treatment will have a lasting impact on the human suffering, shame, ruination, loss of dignity, and even the loss of the lives of the problem gamblers.

Evidence-Based Programs/Services

Evidenced-based services are essential to a successful program. These services include, but are not limited to:

- Triage
- Cognitive Behavioral Therapy
- Motivational Interviewing
- Recovery Skills
- Relapse Prevention
- Social Skills Training
- Behavioral Self-Management
- Bibliotherapy
- Twelve-Step Facilitation
- Stress Management
- Anger Management
- Individual Therapy
- Group Therapy
- Family Therapy
- Supportive-Expressive Psychotherapy
- Intensive Case Management
- Voucher Based Reinforcement Therapy

Examples of gambling specific groups are Basics of Gambling Addiction, Identifying Gambling Triggers, Gambling Specific Relapse Prevention, Finances, Legal Aspects of Gambling, Life Story, Goodbye Letter to the Gambling Addiction, Gambling Effects on the Family, Erroneous Thoughts, Journaling, Reel Therapy, Women's/Men's Process Groups, Anger Management (one example: gambling addiction and domestic violence), Impulse Control Disorders, Neurophysiology, and Discharge or Continuing Care and Recovery Planning. Using appropriate journals and workbooks are encouraged in journaling. There are many available. These can be gambling specific or include books focused on cognitive behavioral therapy, finances, maintenance, or relapse prevention. Reel Therapy consists of approved or appropriate films and documentaries apropos to the education and treatment of pathological gambling.

Services and Target Populations

Pathological gamblers requiring residential treatment have likely reached a point at which they need a safe haven to protect them from the stigma and anger of friends, family, coworkers and others. They may be unable to accomplish basic activities of daily living or function successfully in society. The residential facility affords them a safe, stable environment in which to learn the tools to get and remain gambling-free. The facility provides space and time, allowing the gambler to focus on individual recovery. It also allows treatment providers to supervise the activities and observe the mood of the client. Clients in residential care generally are unable to get and/or remain gambling-free at a lower level of care. Residential care may be indicated for clients exhibiting suicidal ideation or gestures

Residential treatment provides 24-hour support and supervision. Staff observations and the client's self-report will be instrumental in treatment planning and case management. Credentialed problem gambling counselors will provide evidence-based treatment in many areas, specifically Cognitive Behavioral therapy to deal with the distorted thinking of the gambler. It takes a village to treat a pathological gambler and residential care is that village, providing a base from which to make appropriate referrals, e.g., primary medical care providers, psychiatrists, psychologists, social services providers, employment assistance and legal aid.

Evaluation

Success in residential treatment is determined by the ability of the client to utilize the tools and techniques learned in treatment in everyday life when confronted by high risk situations, triggers and temptations. Another important indicator is compliance with the recovery plan.

Agency Capacity

Residential programs, and their capacities, will vary according to location, population, financial resources and available community resources. An important determining factor is the availability of qualified staff. For example, in Nevada, counselor qualifications are defined in the Nevada Revised Statutes (NRS) and the Nevada Administrative Code (NAC). In Nevada qualified staff includes Certified Problem Gambling Counselors or Certified Problem Gambling Counselor Interns, Licensed Clinical Social Workers, a Master's level Nurse or a Licensed Marriage and Family Therapist who has been licensed pursuant to NRS chapter 641A, or a Psychologist or a Licensed Alcohol and Drug Abuse Counselor, licensed pursuant to NRS chapter 641C.

If appropriate funding is not available, creative use of various community resources, online programs, and support groups of all types could be compiled to make a workable program for an individual client.

Collaboration

It is important to collaborate with a variety of community resources, specifically other social service and public health agencies. They may have levels of care that are not present in your agency as well as access to other needed services and resources.

Admission Criteria

Prior to admission, the client will receive a comprehensive assessment. Any qualified mental health professional can perform this assessment. The assessment will address the six dimensions of the Gambling Patient Placement Criteria (GPPC):

Dimension 1: Frequency/Intensity/Duration of Disorder

Dimension 2: Biomedical Conditions/Complications

Dimension 3: Cognitive/Behavioral/Emotional Conditions

Dimension 4: Readiness to Change

Dimension 5: Relapse or Continued Problem History/Potential

Dimension 6: Current Recovery/Living Environment

Based on the cumulative scores, the assessor will recommend LOC III for the client if so warranted. For example, high scores (a score of 7, 8, or 9) in multiple dimensions might suggest residential placement.

Patient placement using the GPPC is a result of a careful and comprehensive screening, assessment, evaluation and diagnosis process. The APA's DSM-IV, is used to assure accurate clinical diagnosis. A comprehensive and differential diagnosis using DSM-IV multiaxial assessment can be enhanced by GPPC dimensional evaluation.

Case Study

The client, Kay Syrah, is a 62-year-old White female, who lives in Reno, Nevada. The client was referred to treatment by her probation officer. She is currently on probation for theft, as she stole jewelry from a friend, pawned the items, and subsequently used the money to fund her gambling. Gambling treatment has been ordered by the court and is part of her probation. Kay had a long career in banking, working for a major American company for 40 years. She retired at age 62 and is now living solely on her Social Security retirement benefits. Her 401K had been depleted over the last five years due to her borrowing against it and using the money playing her favorite game, the "Lady Di" slot machines. Kay had found it more and more difficult to concentrate on her job as she was spending more and more time thinking of her next gambling episode, recalling her past wins and planning how to get money with which to gamble.

Mrs. Syrah began gambling five years ago after the unexpected death of her husband of 30 years. She began spending all of her time in the casinos. She enjoyed the crowds and felt calm and relaxed when she played the slot machines. The casino employees also made her feel special, calling her by her first name, and often providing free drinks, meals, and sometimes even a free room. She began by playing penny slots one penny at a time. She quickly began betting five dollars per bet, then $100 per bet. She needed to gamble with increased amounts of money to feel the high of being in action. She had been gambling only a few months when she hit her first big win. She won $12,000 on the dollar slot machines. This was followed by several smaller wins. At this time she felt she could earn a living doing what she loved, gambling. It was then she decided to take early retirement. Her winning streak soon ended. She mortgaged her home which ultimately was foreclosed on by the bank. When this money was gone she took a title loan on her car because she knew she was "due" for a big win. After all, the casino owed it to her. Her biggest loss occurred three weeks after her big win when she put $10,000 in the slot machines one weekend.

Upon the loss of her car, Kay became very depressed. She was now homeless and penniless. She began drinking more, and her loneliness increased. Her parents are deceased, and her two children no longer speak to her because she has "gambled away their inheritance." She no longer has friends because she spends all her time in the casinos and no longer has contact with them. Her best friend no longer speaks to her because Kay stole jewelry from her and pawned it.

She has developed high blood pressure and gastrointestinal problems. She has lost her appetite and has great difficulty sleeping. She is angry, irritable, and dysphoric, cannot concentrate, and has intense gambling cravings.

She described having fanciful suicidal ideations. Kay states she would rather be dead than live in a homeless shelter. She has been imagining ways she might end her life if she should become homeless. Currently Kay denies suicidal ideation, intent, plan or means.

GPPC Dimensional Assessment

Dimension 1: Frequency/Intensity/Duration of Disorder   Current: 8 HIGH

The client states she never gambled until the death of her husband five years ago when she was 57. Kay's gambling quickly escalated from an hour or two on the weekends to gambling daily, sometimes 12 or more hours each day. On one or two occasions she even spent over 36 hours at her favorite machine, the "Lady Di" slot machine. Her biggest win occurred two months into her gambling career when she won $12,000. Her biggest loss was approximately six months ago when she lost the last $10,000 of the money she received from mortgaging her home. She has subsequently lost her car and is currently homeless and penniless with the exception of her Social Security benefits. She prefers playing the slot machines because it makes her forget that her husband is no longer with her. Kay currently reports feeling angry, irritable and sad, and states she has intense cravings and difficulty concentrating. She reports difficulty sleeping and feels tired all of the time. She denies the use of any illegal, prescribed or over the counter drugs. She denies a problem with alcohol although she admits to drinking more and more the past few months.

Dimension 2: Biomedical Conditions/Complications   Current: 4 MODERATE

The client presents as an age-appropriate 62-year-old female. She was well groomed and neatly dressed. She looked tired and had dark circles under her eyes. She states she had been in relatively good health her entire life up until a few years ago. Her health deteriorated at the same rate as her savings account. Both plummeted to rock bottom approximately six months ago when she lost her home and subsequently, $10,000, the last of the money from mortgaging her home. Kay has not been to a doctor since discovering she has high blood pressure. Currently she has no insurance. She quit her job, cannot afford health insurance payments, and is not yet eligible for Medicare, due to her age. She also has no doctor at this time. Her gastrointestinal problems increased upon the loss of her car. This has resulted in a major weight loss. She is on no prescribed or over-the-counter medications. She denies the use of any illegal drugs. She denies any family history of chronic disease. There are no conditions that would influence her ability to participate in or complete treatment.

Dimension 3: Cognitive/Behavioral/Emotional Conditions   Current: 8 HIGH

The client denies ever having been diagnosed with a mental health disorder. Kay denies any physical or sexual abuse or being a victim or perpetrator of any domestic violence. She denies any family history of mental illness.

Mrs. Syrah is currently serving three years' probation on a theft conviction. Her Probation Officer is Officer Begood. One year ago she stole jewelry from a friend and pawned it. She did not mean to do her friend any harm. She simply "borrowed" the items and intended get them out of pawn and return them before her friend found out. She had depleted her bank account and could "feel" a big win coming. She has no other criminal history.

She has a Master's Degree in Business Administration. She worked for a major American commercial banking company for 40 years until she retired at age 62. She was having a great deal of difficulty concentrating on her job, and had been tempted at times to "borrow" some money from the bank without going through proper channels. She felt retiring would be a better option and that she could then gamble full time to supplement her Social Security benefits.

Kay states she has been on a one year losing streak that has affected all areas of her life. She has no friends because she had no time for them this past year due to spending all her time in casinos. She would lie and make excuses so often they finally quit including her in their plans. Her best friend no longer speaks to Kay since the theft of her jewelry, and her children are "fed up" with her because, according to them, she has "spent their inheritance." During the past year she has lost both her home and her car due to her gambling. She states she is getting more and more depressed, and would rather die than live in a homeless shelter. She began making a variety of plans in order to achieve this goal. At the current time there has been recurrent ideation but no lethal plan. If not for gambling, she would not even get dressed in the morning. She has no prior attempts at suicide, although there had been some ideation at the time of her husband's death.

Kay states her entire identity was that of a wife and a bank manager. She states she becomes more depressed each day, feeling she no longer has an identity. She admits to drinking more and more to alleviate the loneliness and depression. She reports experiencing a great deal of shame and guilt. The fact that she is living on very little money only adds to the depression. At this point she is living on her Social Security and her comps at the casinos, and these are almost depleted.

Dimension 4: Readiness for Change   Current: 6 MODERATE
The client came to the assessment to fulfill conditions of her probation. She was amicable and pleasant during the interview. Kay admits to gambling daily for the past year. She is able to acknowledge that the loss of her house and car was the direct result of her gambling, but she is confident her big win is just around the corner, and that then "everything will be all right." She does not want to quit gambling entirely, but states she would be willing to try anything to alleviate the depression and loneliness. Besides, she does not want to go to jail. Since she is homeless and has no place to go, she is amenable to residential treatment. The client appears to be in the Contemplation Stage of Change and is more externally motivated than internally motivated. At this point Kay still sees more advantages to gambling than quitting. However, she is willing to try treatment at this time. She feels she will feel safer and less lonely with other people around.

Dimension 5: Relapse or Continued Problem History/Potential   Current: 8 HIGH
The client's game of choice is the "Lady Di" slot machine. Kay first played the game five years ago at age 57, upon the death of her husband. She played at the Aquarius Casino in Reno, Nevada. She finds solace and friendship in the casinos without really having to have any interactions with others and, thus, no responsibilities regarding social obligations. Living in Reno affords her the opportunity to gamble 24 hours a day, seven days a week. If she does not feel like going to a casino there are also the supermarkets, gas stations, drug stores, etc., where she can play.

For the past year Kay has been gambling daily. She receives her Social Security check on the third of each month, and the money rarely lasts more than a week. She has been spending up to $500 per gambling episode and has depleted both her other retirement account and the money she received from mortgaging her home which she lost to foreclosure. Although she worked as a bank manager for 40 years, she had frequently overdrawn her checking account, and the bank finally closed the account.

One of the factors in deciding to take early retirement was the fact that Kay could not concentrate on her job. She was so preoccupied with planning her next gambling venture and/or thinking about past experiences and her big win that she began making more and more mistakes. An audit revealed a series of mistakes and she was written up. She felt she could do better on her own in the casinos and that she would find the experience more rewarding.

She began playing the penny slot machines, a penny at a time. She quickly progressed to quarter machines and then to dollar machines. After losing her 401K, her home, and her car, Kay continued to go back to recoup her losses. She states she just knows she is due for another big win.

Kay's triggers are loneliness, boredom and ready money. She has had no prior treatment for either gambling or depression. She has no family history of gambling.

Dimension 6: Current Recovery/Living Environment   Current: 8 HIGH

At this point Kay is no longer employed. She took early retirement to pursue her gambling career. She has been living in weekly hotels and using her comps at various casinos since depleting all sources of funds. At this point she has no assets. She has lost her home and her car due to her gambling.

Kay's parents are deceased. She is an only child. Her husband died unexpectedly five years ago. Her children, John aged 45, and Mary, aged 43, no longer speak to her because they feel she has gambled away their inheritance. She is estranged from all her friends. She has no support system of any kind.

Kay is currently on probation and she is court-ordered to treatment as part of her probation agreement.

Driving Dimensions: 1, 3, 5, 6

The client presents with a relatively rapid onset of gambling activity upon the death of her husband five years ago. She is estranged from her family and friends and has no support system. She has given up her job, home, automobile, friends and all her savings to pursue her career in gambling. At this point she is unable to stop or control the gambling.

Suicidality; Threat to Self/Others: Current: 6 MODERATE

Kay admits to increasing instances of suicidal ideation as her loneliness increases and her finances decrease. She is overcome with shame and guilt and "wants the pain to go away." She has made no attempts, but her plans are becoming more and more concrete.

Vulnerabilities/Strengths:

Vulnerabilities: The client is virtually homeless and living on a fixed income. Kay has had no prior treatment and does not possess the tools necessary to get and remain gambling free. She doesn't really want to quit gambling, but realizes she is in a dire financial situation. She also understands that she is becoming more and more depressed. In addition there is a court order for treatment. She does not want to go to jail.

Strengths: The client is well educated and possesses good social skills. She states she is amenable to treatment at this time. She was focused, responsive and cooperative throughout the interview.

Assessment Instruments Used and Results:

The client answered "Yes" to 8 out of 10 items on the **DSM-IV gambling screen.** Five or more "Yes" answers on this instrument meets diagnostic criteria for 312.31 Pathological Gambling. She answered "Yes" to 14 out of 20 on the **South Oaks Gambling Screen (SOGS).** Answering "Yes" to five or more items on this instrument indicates "probable pathological gambling." In addition she gave two "Yes" answers to the **Lie/Bet questions.** "Yes" to one or both questions on this screen indicates the need for further assessment. The client was also administered the **Substance Abuse Subtle Screening Inventory (SASSI),** which did not indicate a High Probability of having a Substance Dependence Disorder, but did support a diagnosis of Substance Abuse using the DSM-IV diagnostic criteria. A complete biopsychosocial assessment was also administered.

Clinical Impressions:
DSM-IV MULTIAXIAL ASSESSMENT

- Axis I: 312.31 Pathological Gambling
           305.00 Alcohol Abuse
  Rule Out Bi-Polar Disorder
  Rule Out Sleep Disorder

- Axis II: V71.09 No diagnosis on Axis II

- Axis III: Rule Out Hypertension
  Rule Out Acid Reflux Disease

- Axis IV: Death of husband, estrangement from children
  Estrangement from friends, inadequate social support, living alone
  Adjustment to retirement
  Unemployed, unsuccessful gambling career
  Inadequate housing
  Inadequate finances
  Inadequate health care services, inadequate health insurance
  Arrest, litigation, probation
  Discord with Probation Officer

- Axis V: GAF 35 (highest level in past year)

The client began gambling upon the unexpected death of her husband five years ago. During the past year Kay's gambling escalated to daily gambling with amounts of up to $500 per episode. She stole and pawned her friend's jewelry to obtain money with which to gamble. She has lied to her friends regarding her gambling and has avoided them. She becomes irritable, restless and angry when she is unable to gamble. She is manifesting gastrointestinal problems along with high blood pressure. She was so preoccupied with her gambling that she was unable to concentrate at work so she took an early retirement to devote all her time to gambling. She was certain she could earn a living.

The past year was a losing streak. Kay lost her home, her car, her money, and her relationships with her children and all her friends. She also lost her self-esteem and sense of identity. She went deeper and deeper into a depression that resulted in recurrent suicidal ideation. The client is also court ordered for treatment as part of her probation agreement.

Based on assessment instrument results and clinical interview, this client meets diagnostic criteria for 312.31 Pathological Gambling and 305.00 Alcohol Abuse. Treatment is strongly recommended.

Reports Made; Consents Given:
At the client's request, and with a signed release, a copy of this report was sent to Probation Officer Begood.

Provisional Treatment Plan & Discharge/Transition Criteria:

This client would benefit from GPPC Level III residential treatment. She will be assigned to both the Gambling Track for her pathological gambling and the Substance Track for her alcohol abuse. The residential unit will afford her a safe haven wherein she can learn the tools to get and remain both gambling free and substance free. Most importantly it will provide her with the socialization to work on her self-esteem and reduce her sense of aloneness.

Additional Information:

Dianne Springborn, MA, CPGC-S, LCADC-S completed this assessment at Bristlecone Family Resources, McCarran Campus, on September 14, 2009.

VI
Family and Legal Issues

Vignette

A Typical Client with Legal Issues

Susie Cue is a 50-year-old married Hispanic female living with her husband in Reno, Nevada. The client was referred for an evaluation of her self-reported gambling problem by her Nevada State Parole and Probation Officer, following Susie's release from prison. Susie was imprisoned for three years after being arrested for embezzling $203,150 from her employer. Susie states she did not gamble while in prison and her last bet was three years ago. At that time, she had one-day wins and losses of up to $4000 playing video poker. She had been gambling daily for nearly four years. She states her gambling began as recreational when she was 21, and increased significantly after her mother died of cancer and that she has experienced marital distress as a result. Susie admits she did not fully address her grief and loss issues with herself, her husband, or any other resources such as her church support system or any mental health professional. Instead, she used gambling as a way to escape from her emotional pain and to avoid feelings altogether. Susie did not receive any evaluation for her gambling at the time of her conviction for embezzlement. She states she attempted to get a Gamblers Anonymous meeting started in prison, but it did not occur while she was there. She admits she still has some marital and financial distress which she believes could be a trigger to relapsing to gambling, although she has been involved with Gamblers Anonymous since she got out of prison. She has had no other treatment for her emotional or behavioral addiction issues besides hospitalization for a suicide attempt following her arrest three years ago. She is willing to accept treatment now.

Discussion

Problem Statement

Problem and compulsive or pathological gambling affects problem gamblers and their families in a variety of ways, such as finances and interpersonal relationships. All of these effects of problem gambling are negative. Where once gambling represented socializing or entertainment within a family's traditions and activities, the effects of problem and pathological gambling eat away at the tapestry that weaves the family together like a pernicious infestation of bugs. Once an individual has developed problems with gambling behavior, multi-layered consequences begin affecting family members, co-workers and employers, friends, and any other interpersonal relationships. Although the problem gambler in denial may not notice or admit that gambling problems bother others, in fact the consequences are significant. This chapter will outline gambling problems within a family or group of significant others.

Contributing Factors:

Many factors contribute to the personal, interpersonal and social consequences of problem gambling. The affected individual, the family and the surrounding social system experience tremendous disturbance, upheaval and distress. Individual well-being, family coherence, and social functioning are placed in jeopardy by covert and overt responses to increasingly perilous circumstances. A spouse or significant other may feel threatened by misperceived infidelity or by suspicions of theft, lying or duplicity on the part of the partner. Inappropriate responses based on these perceptions can contribute to accelerated dysfunction within the family system. Control, always a critical issue for problem gamblers, becomes confounded and distorted by the fear of loss of control. Eventually the actions and reactions of the gambler, the spouse, the family, and the surrounding social system can become driven by fear, anger and blaming.

The people affected by one problem gambler often include the following, even when the others do not yet know about the gambling problem:

- Spouse, partner, or significant other
- Parents
- In-laws
- Children
- Siblings
- Ex- and step-family members
- Employers
- Co-workers
- Teachers
- Students
- Business customers and/or partners
- Church members and church leaders
- Friends (especially those the gambler borrows from)
- Health-care professionals treating the gambler
- Legal entities: police, judges, probation officers, etc.
- Financial entities involved with the gambler
- Lending institutions: banks, pawn shops, "payday loan" companies
- Gaming entities: especially hosts and managers

The above list may appear to some to include nearly everyone in the community surrounding the problem gambler. The disorder, distress and dysfunction of problem gambling affect everyone in the social constellation. Impulse control disorders and addictions do not occur in a vacuum. Everyone connected is affected. That is one of the intentions of this book: to illustrate the breadth and depth problem gambling can reach in any community. All people encountering problem gambling can benefit from increased education and awareness about the signs of the problem, its consequences, and the resources that can be used to address and relieve the distress of those involved in the problem.

Affected friends and family of problem gamblers are often first encountered by health care and financial professionals. Family members may be asking for help with a concern they have about the gambler, such as drug treatment to reduce cravings or how to protect what is left of the assets after a problem gambler has drained much of the family's finances. Another reason family members seek health care or financial counseling is because they are suffering signs of stress due to the gambler's actions.

With appropriate resources a family doctor or banker could refer the family to specific information about the problem, such as information about how to cope with a loved one who gambles, or a referral to a credit counselor or attorney for financial guidance. Publications such as "Personal Financial Strategies for the Loved Ones of Problem Gamblers," prepared by the National Endowment for Financial Education, can be very helpful. Without expert knowledge, healthcare and financial professionals could still be useful in steering family members toward proper care. Quite often, however, those well-meaning healthcare and financial professionals are not familiar with problem gambling, its signs and symptoms, or the treatment and interventions available, i.e., they cannot share information they do not have. The GPPC manual is designed to help anyone in contact with a problem gambler to learn more about recognizing and responding to the disorder and directing the gambler or the family member toward obtaining appropriate assistance and care. Helpful information and treatment is available for the concerned professional or helper, the family member, and the gambler.

Family members are not always aware that they need of some kind of assessment or evaluation themselves. Family may be conscious of being upset or aggravated by unfortunate events caused by the gambling problem. However, they often believe that the solution for their aggravation is to "fix the gambler," and following that cure, the family will all feel better. There is a kernel of truth in this idea, surrounded by denial and a lack of information. Family members regularly appear to resemble war survivors: they are shell-shocked or traumatized and yet still functioning at some level. Family members usually have numerous psychological and/or physical side-effects or after-effects from problem gambling, even though they may not yet have developed their own addiction or disordered behavior. Often family members will describe upset stomachs, agitation and anxiety, anger, depression, confusion, and thoughts of harming themselves or others. Without further investigation, the family members could manifest more serious psychological, physical and legal problems than the problem gambler. However, family members may not know they are at such risk until they are screened or assessed by a professional. The authors believe that anyone affected by problem gambling, close family members in particular, should be assessed for their own problems in the physical, psychological, legal and spiritual arenas, and should seek appropriate treatment as needed.

Intended Outcomes

In discussing their needs in a counseling setting, family members have commented that they have certain common and primary needs. Immediately, and for the duration of living with problem gambling, they need information and support. When a spouse calls a treatment center asking for help for the gambler, it is usually apparent that the non-gambling spouse is in a great deal of distress, including shock, anger, confusion, betrayal, fear, and transition, to name a few. The non-gambling spouse often feels pressured to make an immediate decision about many important things such as whether to allow the gambler to stay in the home, whether to close bank accounts or freeze assets in some way to preclude further family losses, and whether to involve the legal system, if money has been stolen. Because the gambler betrayed the trust of the non-gambling spouse, emotions run to extremes, and the danger of further harm is great. It is our opinion that a brief assessment of the non-gambler's needs is essential.

In a gambling treatment setting, family members who agree will be assessed right along with the gambler. The assessment process begins with a professional screening. This screening often includes questionnaires the client fills out to share the history of both the effects of the gambling on the individual as well as other personal background. This can include family history of addiction of any kind, family history of abuse or violence, family history of financial or work-related problems, family history of mental illness, family history of legal problems or incarceration, family history of medical or physical problems, and the current level of medical, mental health, support group, spiritual, work-related or legal involvement. The assessment professional that has the opportunity to interview both the gambler and family members together or within a short time of the gambler's initial interview gains a great deal of perspective of the individual and family needs of each member. We highly recommend getting the family involved at the assessment level. The clinician can quickly and easily observe verbal and non-verbal indicators that family members may need further assessment and referral for appropriate treatment.

The assessment professional should obtain written consent to collaborate with and get collateral information from family members at the initial interview, and enlist the gambler's cooperation in sharing certain information between the treatment center, the gambler, and the family. Giving the gambler some guidance on the value of collateral information and assurance that it will solely concern the gambler's wants and needs is important. A refusal to share information with family members at this point may suggest possible treatment or intervention strategies needed next. For example, the gambler may be afraid to share the full extent of his or her losses with the family, and may believe he or she will be kicked out or further punished when this information comes to light. A limited consent to share information still may be obtained, wherein the counselor identifies exactly what the client agrees to disclose.

The GPPC Initiative has found that family information and involvement is essential to determining the success of the gambler in treatment. In short, having a gambler and family members involved together in treatment will produce significant positive change. Family members may be reluctant to get into a treatment group or into their own individual treatment although they readily admit they are angry and upset. It will take a bit of education and exposure to different types of treatment and support modalities for many family members to engage themselves fully in the recovery effort. We believe the element of time is an important factor. Keep inviting, give it some time, offer several kinds of entry points for the family, and eventually they are likely to appreciate and benefit from what they find.

Inviting family members to immediately attend a support group, in particular Gam-Anon, is a recommendation we make in the first phone call or visit we have with them. It is useful to keep handouts, phone-lists, website information, and directions to nearby meetings ready to share with them to provide what they need to make informed decisions about their future attendance. Those family members who attend family programs in treatment, including Gam-Anon, are most likely to feel better, learn more, and stay together longer (for those living with problem gamblers). If the gambler and the family are not able to stay together, the family members still survive the changes better if they attend the family program and Gam-Anon. In some outpatient and residential treatment settings for gambling addiction, the family component of treatment includes education meetings, 12-Step meetings, therapy groups, individual and couples or family therapy, and more. The more the family learns and experiences, the better the treatment outcome. Some treatment programs, such as those provided by the Reno Problem Gambling Center, are looking forward to a comprehensive Family Intensive Outpatient Program for the families of gamblers, and some have started hybrid programs, found them to be successful, and are pursuing funding to make a full Family IOP program a reality.

In combined family- and gambling-client groups in an intensive outpatient setting, the identification and definition of addiction includes addressing co-dependence or co-addiction. When the family members hear their stories compared with their gambler's stories, there are a variety of possible reactions. Family members may be annoyed and yet relieved to learn they have to address their own co-addiction, not just the identified patient's addiction. A therapeutic, psycho-educational group process illuminates and offers a safe place to discuss and learn more about these ideas. It takes time and repetition, and lots of education, to generate growth.

The group education/therapy process environment is a rich and useful place for this kind of growth to occur. Many family members declare that it greatly helped them both understand their spouse's addiction and understand their own part in the disorder. Ongoing, family member/gambler groups in conjunction with separate co-addicted and gamblers groups generate synergy in recovery. In other words, putting gamblers into a treatment program alone is less likely to produce positive results. The family's awareness and treatment helps the gambler and the family to heal and grow.

Evidence-based Programs/Services: What Has Worked

Here are some of the family-oriented methods the authors have used and found helpful:

- Invite family and friends to every level of treatment, from the first phone contact or visit, so that they may learn, participate, and also be assessed for their own treatment needs.

- Screen and assess family along with the gambler and/or separate from the gambler, as the occasion permits.

- Obtain consent to release information between the gambler and the family members and the treatment/assessment professional according to the needs and wants of each, after discussing pros/cons.

- Enlist the family to be available for future phone conversations to both collaborate and offer further information at all stages of treatment for the gambler and the family by obtaining all possible phone, email, and address information at the first opportunity.

- Teach the willing family members as much as possible about the disorder of pathological gambling. Teach at every opportunity, including the phone calls and mailings sent.

- Share professional experience about the understanding you have that the family is impacted, affected, and involved in the disorder of pathological gambling, and thus deserves and requires ongoing assessment and education for family's needs.

- Have information about these resources, explained in detail, with phone numbers, directions and references printed for the family to do their own research and ready to be handed out or mailed to each inquiring family or friend.

- Show the family a "tour" of your facility, through virtual means or in person, that they may quickly know what treatment resources you have at hand.

- Discover the family's level of understanding including checking the barriers and gateways to any treatment communications.

- Have success stories handy, both in writing and with permission by phone, so that inquiries can be made to actual persons who have experienced treatment and are willing to share their stories.

- Gather data and be prepared to share numbers. Outcomes, especially how your own program has done, are very important to prospective clients.

- Normalize their experience by listening to their fears and immediately offering your observations of how they compare to others you have treated, and invite them again to sit and listen and see for themselves how treatment works.

- Explain the assessment process in whatever detail they desire, including showing them each of the forms and explaining the utility of assessment for them and their loved ones and that more than one assessment is usually recommended, for ongoing appropriate treatment.

- If a gambler or family member does not return after the initial assessment, follow up with a phone call and/or a letter in a few days and then again at 30-day intervals, at least once, to offer support and further information.

- Share your experiences in assessing family and gamblers with other professionals and give yourself and your team-members credit for intervening, educating, and planting seeds of knowledge with people who really need you.

- Offer resources immediately available to the gambler and the family, including the Problem Gamblers HelpLine (800-522-4700), a confidential 24-hour help line. Offer information on the various levels of treatment and support in the immediate area.

Services and Target Populations: Our Proposal

The GPPC is a beneficial tool for family members as well as problem gamblers. There are components that are applicable immediately, as mentioned previously, for education, understanding, and assisting in meeting the needs of the family members who are curious and concerned about how the treatment process works. The components specific to family that we find very useful include screening instruments or interview questions that can check the mental status and personal needs of the family member who may be in distress at that moment. Should the family member agree to being assessed, and should that family member need some kind of treatment, the prompts found on the Counselor's Working Aid sheet (see GPPC Manual Module) are excellent to be used in determining what areas of concern there are for the family member and what treatment options might be beneficial. A credentialed professional able to assess suicidality and other urgent needs could use the PLAID PALS screening sheet (see Screening/Assessment Instruments Module) as a prompt for evaluating their current suicidal ideation. The caring professional can also simply walk the family member through the family information sections of the assessment forms and explain how useful their collateral information can be in achieving honesty in treatment. Getting family history from the family members directly is wonderfully helpful for the therapist involved in the gambler's care.

Once the GPPC assessment has been completed, the professional is able to explain immediately the diagnosis and level of care recommended for the client. The beauty of the GPPC as a screening and level-of-care placement tool is its utility in the present moment, when the client and family are present and ready to receive treatment direction.

Our Successes

The gambling experts who created this book, namely the GPPC team, have each experienced success stories in using the GPPC. We wish first to thank the counselors in Nevada who were willing to implement the GPPC in its fledgling stages, and gave us feedback in the focus groups as we worked the bugs out of each revision. Bristlecone Family Resources, for example, has an independent residential and outpatient gambling program called the "GATE" (Gambling Addiction Treatment and Education) program, with treatment available from Level 0.5 through Level 3 (See GPPC Manual Module for Levels of Care). GATE counselors have commented that using the GPPC is very helpful to determine the appropriate level of care for the client. Many practitioners in Nevada, where the GPPC was first tested, have noted that a GPPC narrative was the smoothest, quickest format for transferring a client to a different treatment location. The GPPC affords all the necessary demographics that professionals require for a quick assessment on the first page. It also provides further dimensional information in appropriate detail that other treatment professionals can use to immediately ascertain the gambling patient's needs.

Evaluation

The best evaluation of interventions by and for the family of problem gamblers is determined by the family itself. Reduction of acute stressors, improved quality of life and improved family functionality are the best indicators of effective interventions. The practitioner may evaluate these improved outcomes from a clinical perspective, but the true benchmark is whether or not the family can see that what they are doing is working.

Agency Capacity

The treatment provider must have adequate space and time to conduct couple's and family interventions. The agency staff must include credentialed professionals able to perform couple's marriage and family therapy in addition to problem gambling counseling.

Collaboration

Problem gambling counselors working with couples and families must rely on extensive connections in and with the surrounding community to access and provide a wide range of social support services for the family. These will of course extend beyond the clinical presenting problem and may include financial counseling, legal counseling, housing and child-care support services, transportation, and medical services.

The Future

The GPPC team envisions a number of different professionals finding the GPPC useful. As has been seen with the ASAM PPC-2R, healthcare professionals such as insurance reviewers will now have a framework on which to base a discussion with counselors, hospitals and other treatment agencies regarding their gambling patients. The language of the GPPC dimensions will afford easier discussion of the patient's changing needs.

Since family members are often involved in the gambling patient's care, in particular continuing care and lowering levels of care as the patient works through treatment, the GPPC becomes useful for the patient and the family working with the doctor, counselor, or other healthcare professional to review and plan for individual patients' needs. The GPPC is a confidential document, however many couples find the clarity of treatment planning together to be helpful for both parties. As honesty is an integral part of recovery from pathological gambling, sharing the treatment plan as part of counseling is also important.

Legal Issues

One of the Gamblers Anonymous 20 Questions and one of the DSM-IV 10 diagnostic questions asks if the person has committed illegal acts to fund gambling. This is an unfortunate and disturbing aspect of the person's descent into the chaos of problem gambling. Quite often the gambler will not only lie and cheat, but also steal to keep the funds flowing and to be able to gamble another day. When individuals commit crimes related to gambling, such as embezzlement, and are brought before the court to be tried, it often happens that the defense, the prosecution and the judge may be unaware that the crime is related to gambling. Because of shame, stigma, or disbelief in the illness of pathological gambling, people in the legal arena may ignore or dismiss the effects of pathological gambling as they relate to the crime.

A judge in Reno, Nevada who has been helping alcoholics and addicts in his own specialty court for many years shared with the GPPC team that he cannot order an evaluation for the defendant's possible gambling problem unless the word "gambling" appears in the arrest report. It is imperative that members of the legal community begin asking questions about money and gambling problems whenever a domestic disturbance, robbery, fraud, or other crime occurs that may be the result of a person's problem with gambling. Once the offender is identified as a potential problem gambler, the courts can move forward with an evaluation from a professional mental health worker, who may diagnose and suggest treatment for the gambler.

In 2009, Nevada revised the existing diversion law and now allows judges to order evaluations and sanctions for those who commit crimes related to gambling. If offenders are found to be pathological gamblers and meet certain eligibility criteria, the court can order a court-supervised plan for treatment and restitution. This law, NRS 458A, "Prevention and Treatment of Problem Gambling," allows persons who commit crimes relating to gambling, who fit the parameters of the law and successfully complete treatment and court mandates, to have their criminal history sealed. This is a great benefit for those caught in the snare of problem gambling who are ready to make restitution and benefit from treatment.

A GPPC evaluation completed by a trained professional will afford both the defense and the judge sufficient information to make informed choices regarding the sentencing of the defendant who is both diagnosed a pathological gambler and appropriate for treatment and restitution plans under the court's orders. This process began with Judge Mark Farrell's gambling court in Amherst, New York in September, 2001, when he created the first opportunity for gamblers in the judicial system to be diverted into treatment instead of simply jailed and left without treatment and restitution opportunities.

Using the GPPC in this arena will be immediately helpful to all parties involved. The judge can use the model proposed here, which not only suggests possible treatment and sanctions, but more specifically offers a professional recommendation about the level of care and length of time this individual may need to achieve abstinence and begin his road to recovery.

A Nevada team including the Governor's Advisory Committee on Problem Gambling and its Legal Subcommittee working with the Nevada Council on Problem Gambling has published a tool kit, "Problem Gambling and the Law." The tool kit includes information and guidelines for judges, lawyers, and anyone involved in the legal system as a client to learn more about avenues for help and expert advice regarding criminal issues in problem gambling. Contact the Nevada Council on Problem Gambling online (www.nevcouncil.org) or by telephone (702-369-9740) to receive the latest information.

Case Study

The following case study is based on the experience of several of the GPPC team counselors' experience in working with female gamblers who have committed crimes, and either before or after incarceration, requested treatment for their gambling problems.

Meet Susie Cue: 50-year-old married Hispanic female, ex-felon embezzler and pathological gambler. Susie heard about treatment for her gambling problem while she was serving a three-year sentence for embezzlement in the state prison. While on parole, and with the encouragement of her parole officer, who was acquainted with problem gambling services in Nevada, Susie came to the Reno Problem Gambling Center and requested an evaluation and treatment. Susie's gambling evaluation specifically addressed her legal situation as well as all of the other elements of her personal history which her counselors believe contributed to her current situation.

Susie has never used any other drugs besides alcohol and marijuana, which she used recreationally during college. She quit once she became pregnant with her first child. Since her family history included alcoholism with both parents, she attempted to control her drinking and her evaluation indicated she has never been addicted to alcohol. She also smoked cigarettes as a teenager and quit after a few attempts to "be cool" with the "bad kids," not liking the smell and not getting any perceived benefits from smoking. She was the oldest of three children and did well in school. She took several years of college courses while working full time, eventually dropping out of college after the birth of her second child, and working for a state government office as a manager. Her husband worked full-time and they enjoyed a lifestyle of relative ease, owning their own home and two cars as well as a boat and two motorcycles. Susie eventually had four children and continued to work in different offices, staying the longest with a real estate firm, and becoming very close to the owners. They said they considered her "like family," and she was the best office manager they ever had—enthusiastic, creative, loyal, cheerful—as close to the definition of a girl scout, a mom and a hard-working machine all rolled into one.

When Susie's mom died of cancer, about four years before Susie's arrest, Susie's gambling changed from recreational to daily. She had been going to the casinos whenever family would come to town and she needed to entertain them. The cheap, good food was the draw, but her relatives also liked to gamble, so she would be with them several hours at a time, and found she could pass the time most easily in front of a video poker machine. Susie had played 21 and poker several times with her family when they were younger, as her parents liked to entertain by hosting "bunko," poker or other card games, having pot-luck dinners, and playing other games for many hours on weekends. She never cared for table games when she went out with her friends, but the ease of pushing buttons and occasionally coming home with more than the $20 she brought to the casino to gamble with was pleasant. After she lost her mom, however, Susie found herself going to the casino on her lunch break and stopping after work to "wind down" before going home. Her husband noticed her absence and asked if he could help, but she denied it was a problem. He felt helpless, believed it had something to do with the loss of her mother, and did not want to upset her. He would sometimes meet her at the casino for dinner, and she would gamble for hours, until he either would leave on his own because he was bored or he would try to bring her home and she refused. It was not until many months later that he became aware of the extent of her gambling and tried again to intervene.

When Susie's husband found the credit card statement full of cash advances, he reviewed the bank statement for the status of their checking account. He was planning a motorcycle trip for the two of them as a surprise and needed to make sure they had enough cash for the vacation. He was horrified to find that the balance in their checking was overdrawn and their savings had been used up. He became instantly angry. He started going through the other credit card statements from the past several months and discovered a number of cash advances and another card he did not know they had, with a $10,000 balance on it. That night he confronted her when she got home and they had a loud argument, the first of its kind in their 20-year marriage. She blamed him for being out of line and justified the expenditures for their children's expenses and her need to feel better since her mom died by going shopping more. While her husband was still upset, since the surprise vacation was out of the question, he decided to believe her and let it go. He did not know what else to do so he got a second job to pay off the credit cards.

Susie had been spending so much money gambling that she needed more money than her credit cards or savings could cover. She began writing checks out of a petty-cash account at work, fully intending to put all the money back as soon as she could. Over a period of two years, she did this many times, and kept a separate book to keep track of what she owed. At first she felt nauseated and had difficulty sleeping. Eventually she would return to gamble, lose thousands of dollars, and do the same thing over and over, taking over-the-counter sleeping pills to get to sleep or caffeinated drinks to keep going at work. It was not until she came down with a violent flu and missed three days of work at the same time as an in-house audit that her embezzlement of work funds was revealed. The employer found that she had stolen over $200,000 and he immediately had her arrested. Once she was able to return home and await sentencing, Susie contacted Gamblers Anonymous and says that GA not only saved her life, it gave her the courage she needed to endure the trial and prison time ahead. Susie's husband stayed with her, but two of her four children and her sister-in-law, Barbie, will not speak to her. She is making restitution for the $200,000 and will likely be making restitution payments for the rest of her life.

As she looked back on her behaviors of the past, Susie admits that the turning point for her gambling was not a "big win" like it is for some gamblers she has heard speak in GA and group counseling meetings. She states that the numbness she felt while in front of a video poker machine was the best she had felt in years: it took away all the pain, the loss, the fear, the sadness, and replaced those emotions with a sensation she could only describe as "narcotic." When she would leave the casino after losing all her money and knowing she would have to lie and steal to try to get her losses back, she felt physically ill and went through withdrawal symptoms of agitation, chest pains, breathing difficulties, confusion, nausea, and tremors. As soon she had created her next plan to get the funds she needed to gamble, her physical symptoms diminished and while "in action," anticipating the next opportunity to gamble, she felt normal, albeit agitated. It was only while gambling that Susie felt "good," which as she looks back, was truly a state devoid of feelings, much like someone abusing narcotics. Susie states she was relieved when she was caught. She could finally stop the crazy cycle of chasing and stealing and gambling which had no pleasure for her. She could finally become honest again and try to clean up the lies and betrayal to all her family and friends. Although it was a horrible time, she looks back on the end of her gambling and the time she spent in prison as the best thing that could have happened to her.

When Susie came to the treatment center to obtain an evaluation, she had passed three years without a bet. She was attending Gamblers Anonymous on her own and giving service to GA by chairing a women's meeting once a week. She was working her 12 Steps with a sponsor in GA, and had invited her husband to attend Gam-Anon. He has not yet attended any self-help meetings offered by Gam-Anon or other sources such as his church group. He has been overwhelmed with the work of paying bills and keeping their four children stable while Susie was in prison and with an economic downturn, their home may still be foreclosed on by the bank. His job was barely sufficient to meet their needs, and when Susie got out of prison, she was only able to get hired by temporary agencies who could offer minimum-wage work. Their marriage and family life is suffering because of the pressure of her debts and their financial distress. Below is the dimensional assessment the counselor wrote in her GPPC narrative.

GPPC Dimensional Assessment

Dimension 1: Frequency/Intensity/Duration of Disorder   Current: 2 LOW

No current signs/symptoms of pathological gambling noted/reported. Age 21 began gambling; gambled pathologically four years; last bet three years ago. She denies alcohol, nicotine or other drug abuse. Biggest one-day win: $4000; biggest one-day loss: $4000. Preferred video poker; denies other gambling behaviors. Withdrawal symptoms at the last big loss prior to quitting three years ago included irritability, restlessness, tremors, chest pains, nausea, confusion, cravings and sleep disturbance. Denies current cravings or physical problems.

Dimension 2: Biomedical Conditions/Complications   Current: 1 LOW

Presently describes herself as in a "good, stable" physical condition. Denies any current medication or treatment for any disease. Reports prior prescriptions of Prozac while incarcerated; last used over 12 months ago. Denies sleep or concentration problems at present. Cognitions appear coherent and appropriate; mood appears calm, affect congruent and pleasant, no outward signs of health problems. Denies any injury, surgery, or trauma besides overdose attempt (see Dim. 3).

Dimension 3: Cognitive/Behavioral/Emotional Conditions   Current: 5 MODERATE

Client reports prior diagnosis and treatment of 296.2 major depressive disorder, single episode, when she became suicidal and attempted to overdose with pills three years ago. Treatment at that time was 7 days in a private mental hospital; discharged with Prozac® and Ambien®. Psychiatric care continued while incarcerated; Prozac® continued until 12 months ago. No current complaints of depression or sleep problems. Current marital distress and parenting problems have caused psychological distress and a return to seeking outpatient counseling. Client denies being the perpetrator or victim of domestic violence. Current financial and employment problems reported as causing marital distress. Grief over loss of mother not completely resolved. Client notes mood swings relating to thoughts of mother's death and some fear of contracting cancer. Cumulative incarceration of three years for embezzlement and currently on parole for three years.

Dimension 4: Readiness to Change   Current: 1 LOW

Client is internally motivated and has already demonstrated several behaviors indicating readiness for recovery and positive change, i.e., GA involvement and no gambling for three years. She states a desire for self-improvement, a better marriage, and becoming a better mother are her goals. She appears appropriately concerned for achieving long-term sobriety in GA, making restitution, and working at a job where she can make a decent living. She has been active in GA and volunteers to serve others. She denies cravings for more than two years. She is attempting to alleviate relapse symptoms relating to her current marital and job stressors by attending more GA meetings. She appears to be in the Contemplation stage of change.

Dimension 5: Relapse or Continued Problem History/Potential   Current: 4 MODERATE

Client has successfully maintained abstinence from gambling for three years and denies cravings for at least two years. Her living situation has changed from prison to returning home, which is supportive but is conflicted due to financial stress. She has received no specific education or treatment relative to pathological gambling or relapse prevention. She attends at least 5 GA meetings per week since her release from prison.

Dimension 6: Current Recovery/Living Environment: Current: 6 MODERATE

Client lives at home with husband and two children under the age of 15. Both parents are employed, however client's position is temporary and pays minimum wage. They have very high debts of approximately $100,000 in loans and credit cards, not including their home mortgage and the $200,000 restitution the client owes. Family relations are strained; marital and parental distress is high.

Driving Dimensions: Dimensions 3, 6

Dimensions 3 and 6, based on emotional distress relating to financial, marital and parenting concerns, lack of problem gambling treatment or relapse prevention skills, and uncertainty of stable support system.

Suicidality; Threat to Self/Others: Current: 2 LOW

Client denies current SI/HI plan or intent, states her prior and only attempt at overdose was "a mistake," and she is committed to staying alive for her children. Current risk is low (R1) as evidenced by no recent ideation and strong internal inhibitors as well as seeking assistance from a therapist to deal with current stressors.

Vulnerabilities/Strengths:

Vulnerabilities: Client has had a history of depression and one suicide attempt. Family financial and marital distress has been problematic since she left prison. Client's husband has not agreed to outside support such as Gam-Anon, church, or counseling yet.

Strengths: Client has maintained abstinence and sought support from GA, is active in GA and church, and has voluntarily sought outpatient mental health counseling to cope with financial and marital distress. She is willing to enter into more treatment as directed by professionals.

Assessment Instruments Used and Results:

DSM-IV Screen for Pathological Gambling, lifetime: 10/10 (5 or more "Yes" answers on this instrument meets diagnostic criteria for 312.31 Pathological Gambling); **NODS**, lifetime: 14/17 (Answering "Yes" to five to ten items on this instrument indicates a "pathological gambler"); **SOGS**, lifetime: 15/20 (Answering "Yes" to five or more items on this instrument indicates "probable pathological gambling"); **GA 20 Questions**, lifetime: 20/20 ("Most compulsive gamblers will answer 'Yes' to at least seven of these questions"). Client reports willingness to submit to further mental health assessment with her therapist.

Clinical Impressions:

DSM-IV MULTIAXIAL ASSESSMENT

- Axis I: 312.31, in sustained full remission; rule out 296.2
- Axis II: V71.09 No diagnosis on Axis II
- Axis III: V71.09 No diagnosis on Axis III
- Axis IV: V61.10 Partner Relational Problem; V62.2 Economic problems
- Axis V: GAF: 65 (current)

This client has not gambled in the past three years, thus her pathological gambling is in sustained full remission. However, she never received counseling or education specific to the addiction or to relapse prevention, and is now experiencing marital distress relating to financial problems, reunification after prison, poor work opportunities, and unresolved grief and loss issues. She is willing to begin and be compliant with treatment recommendations.

Reports Made; Consents Given:

Client requested a release of information to authorize sending this assessment with treatment recommendations to her Parole Officer, therapist, and the RPGC Clinical Director. These consents were signed and copies faxed per client's directions.

Provisional Treatment Plan & Discharge Transition Criteria:

Recommended LOC 1, outpatient psychotherapy and psychoeducation, a minimum of three hours per week, including but not limited to 1:1 counseling sessions, couples, family and group counseling. Recommend continuing a minimum of 3 GA meetings per week. Consider transition to lower frequency of outpatient counseling upon successful completion of treatment plan as outlined by agreement of all outpatient therapists involved. Initial focus for treatment on relapse prevention and stress coping strategies.

Summary

As you can see from the dimensions, Susie Cue came into the office in what appeared to be excellent condition. She had overcome the nightmare of arrest, incarceration, and return to her family. She had maintained abstinence from gambling, her mood had improved following the loss of her mother, a suicide attempt, and the separation from her family while in prison, so much so that her Prozac® and Ambien® were gradually reduced and discontinued. However, upon complete assessment of her current situation, the therapist discovered the marital and family distress brewing underneath her calm outward appearance, and recommended more treatment. Susie Cue benefited from this GPPC assessment in several ways, and her family will also be invited to be involved in her ongoing treatment plan. The family will be invited to attend family therapy, marital counseling, psychoeducational groups, and their own assessment for their personal needs. The assessing counselor will offer information and resources available in the community for all of the family, including financial counseling, support services from several agencies including therapeutic, religious, health, government, and educational sources. By inviting all the family to become involved, not only will Susie Cue's prognosis be improved, but each of the family members will have their needs addressed.

VII
Treatment Planning and Treatment

Treatment Planning

The GPPC instrument allows clinicians to do three very important tasks related to treatment planning: document what treatment, if any, has been provided to the client; describe what treatment is provisionally planned for the client; and what goals or outcomes are expected during the current treatment phase. The GPPC is useful during three phases of treatment. The initial GPPC documents the results of screening, assessment, and initial patient placement. The review GPPC gives periodic updates on what goals or outcomes have been achieved, added or modified during the course of treatment. The review GPPC also allows for follow-on stages of treatment and follow-up or outcome assessment, for example at six months or one year post-treatment. The discharge GPPC documents treatment outcomes at successive stages or levels of treatment as the client leaves one level of care for another.

The severity levels of the various dimensions will likely change during and after treatment. The relative severity of any dimension can guide, shift, or prioritize treatment strategies. Changes in severity over time can help to evaluate the efficacy of these strategies. Periodic re-evaluation using the GPPC during treatment can identify significant dimensional changes which may influence the emphases or strategies of treatment. Given the structural compatibility of the GPPC with the placement criteria used by the American Society of Addiction Medicine (ASAM PPC-2R), the GPPC can allow for direct linkage with treatment for co-occurring substance-related disorders, and can be used to track related treatment for other co-occurring mental health disorders.

The treatment plan is more than a description of what the treatment provider intends to do. It describes what services will be provided, the responsibilities and expectations of the client, and the desired treatment outcomes. The GPPC provides a structure for the caring professional to document signs and symptoms at intake; screen, assess, and evaluate the client's presenting problems; plan treatment strategies; document changes in the client's condition; and can be used post-treatment to evaluate treatment outcomes and longer term progress. In effect, the treatment plan is a contract between caring professionals and clients. It is holistic, multidimensional (biopsychosocial and spiritual), dynamic (the plan can change as the client changes), and provides linkages to other service providers (referrals and consultations).

The Substance Abuse and Mental Health Services Administration (SAMHSA) has collaborated through its Addiction Technology Transfer Centers (ATTCs) with the National Institute on Drug Abuse (NIDA) in developing S.M.A.R.T. Treatment Planning. This treatment planning approach is based on five principles: Specific, Measurable, Attainable, Realistic, and Time-limited. These principles correlate very easily with the four basic components of a treatment plan: Problem statements (information obtained from the assessment), Goal statements (derived from the problem statements), Objectives (what the client will do), and Interventions (what the staff will do). The four components of an effective treatment plan will be specific, focusing on particular behaviors or functions. The desired outcomes of the treatment plan will be measurable, attainable, realistic, and time-limited (SAMHSA, 2006).

As noted earlier, the treatment plan is a dynamic document and process beginning with screening and assessment and ending with the discharge plan. It can include initial treatment authorization, level of care determination, referrals, ongoing and additional documentation, periodic treatment plan reviews, and other documents in support of past, present and planned treatment.

Treatment

Pathological gambling, according to the DSM-IV is an impulse control disorder with criteria similar to, yet distinct from, those of substance dependence disorders. "The essential feature of pathological gambling is persistent and recurrent maladaptive gambling behavior that disrupts personal, family, vocational and interpersonal pursuits." A pathological gambler is defined as an individual who exhibits "persistent and recurrent maladaptive gambling behavior as indicated by five (or more) of the following" 10 generalized DSM-IV criteria: preoccupation with gambling, including the anticipation of going gambling; tolerance, which includes betting increasingly larger amounts or taking greater risks to attain the same level of excitement; "repeated, unsuccessful attempts to control, cut back, or stop gambling;" restlessness or irritability "when attempting to cut down or stop gambling;" gambling to escape dysphoric feelings or escape from problems; lying to others to conceal losses; "chasing losses" to get money lost from gambling; committing antisocial, criminal, illegal acts in order to generate money to gamble; jeopardizing relationships, jobs, careers or education because of gambling; and turning to financial "bail outs" from family and others. The DSM-IV also includes the following exclusion criterion for differential diagnosis: "This behavior is not better accounted for by a Manic Episode" (APA, 2000). This allows the clinician to rule out gambling behaviors that may only be present during mood episodes classified elsewhere in the DSM-IV .

A treatment program for problem gambling extends from individual/group outpatient to residential/inpatient treatment for those with the DSM-IV diagnosis of pathological gambling as determined by a comprehensive biopsychosocial assessment. This comprehensive assessment should include both readiness for change determination and whether or not there is a co-occurring disorder associated with the disordered gambling. The GPPC provides a streamlined and guided structure for performing this overall biopsychosocial assessment. Information gathered from the assessment indicates to what degree the client's willingness to explore new and more effective ways to resolve dysfunctional gambling behavior is present. The client's readiness to change and willingness to participate in treatment at this level is a critical factor in successful treatment outcomes. Placement is determined by the intensity of symptoms and the client's level of functioning. Various levels of care are available to enhance treatment progress and potential recovery when other interventions have not succeeded.

A treatment program offers multi-modal, educational, individual, family and group counseling. More intensive treatment is indicated for clients, often in crisis, who require structured, multi-modal (biopsychosocial) treatment. Treatment protocols can include educational groups, individual therapy, group therapy, family therapy, case management, crisis intervention and orientation to Gamblers Anonymous 12-Step, self-help, mutual-support groups. These interventions help to alleviate symptoms, or reduce their severity, and improve a client's level of functioning.

The treatment program provides strategies for motivating clients to enter, continue, and complete treatment. Treatment programs can have a variable length of treatment and have the ability to adjust the clients' frequency of attendance as they progress. Recovering clients are able to resume more of their life obligations while maintaining abstinence from gambling. Client motivation and retention is contingent upon individualized treatment plans which allow both counselor and client to monitor the client's progress toward desired goals and abstinence from gambling. Treatment plans focus on stabilization and transition to community based support groups as needed. Clinicians must be credentialed professionals and sufficiently trained to allow for rapid professional assessment of a change in mental status, life changing developments or resumption of gambling that could warrant a shift to a more intensive level of care.

The targeted and primary aim of intervention and levels of care is abstinence from gambling and the reduction of the significant symptoms and harmful consequences of gambling. Pathological gamblers may come into treatment in a state of panic and crisis. Usually clients enter treatment after they have hit an individual, social, family or financial "bottom." Consequently placement in a structured environment that addresses financial, legal, family, living and psychological issues is necessary and facilitated.

The primary goals of treatment are providing distinct treatment for acute stabilization, engagement, active treatment, group attendance, relapse prevention, treatment planning, and ongoing rehabilitation from gambling. The treatment program focuses on developing coping skills, learning new strategies to deal with urges, treatment planning, money management, the reorganization of thoughts about gambling, restructuring and modifying irrational beliefs about gambling and the odds of winning, relapse prevention, 12-Step self-help GA support groups and Continuing Care support groups. Thus, treatment combines biopsychosocial educational groups, Cognitive-Behavioral group therapy, Behavioral therapy, Motivational Enhancement, Gestalt exercises, individual counseling, video therapy, GA education and encouragement for GA attendance. Throughout the program the emphasis is on accurate individualized treatment planning and continued recovery plans. The crux of this planning is to match individuals and their stage of change with appropriate interventions and treatment strategies. The client-counselor relationship involves negotiating with the clients to find common ground for client-centered care. This requires that the clinician and client accept one another as an equal partner in the treatment process.

Since pathological gambling is a chronic recurring impulse control disorder, the philosophy of treatment is that pathological gambling is treatable. The treatment program will focus on: abstinence; understanding the addictive nature of gambling; clients accepting responsibility for their choices and actions; understanding, conceptualizing and addressing the stages of change; initiating and sustaining new behaviors; shame reduction; involvement of the family; cognitive restructuring by identifying cognitive distortions and errors; and development and empowerment of problem solving skills. Other important components include coping skills training, psychosocial education, impulse management, self-monitoring, and goal setting, and matching the client's range of problems, preferences, expectations and recovery needs with appropriate treatment modalities. Clinicians can extend client-centered care with an introduction to and encouraged attendance at 12-Step GA programs. The treatment program provides an atmosphere of respect and caring wherein each client's inner strengths will be fostered and built upon as problem areas are attended to and remediated.

Services integral to all levels of care are the core services. The treatment program utilizes multi-dimensional treatment modalities. These modalities include:

Behavioral Therapy: teaching stress management, anger management, self-management, identifying high-risk situations, effective steps in problem solving, self-exclusion, operant conditioning of positive and negative reinforcement, impulsiveness, teaching new social skills, goal setting and addressing financial and legal issues.

Gestalt Therapy: using techniques involving staying in the here and now through group process work. It is important for clients to know that the good things in life are not just around the corner after the big win.

In the **Group Process** the healing power is in the clients dealing with the here and now for themselves and the group.

Writing Activities includes the clients writing their own life story. A **Financial History** and **Restitution Plan** is an essential part of a client's recovery. **Interactive Journaling** encourages clients to take ownership of their lives through specific journaling techniques where they find that they are capable and deserving of positive change and that they are the ones who can make that change a possible outcome.

Cognitive Behavioral Therapy which addresses identifying thinking errors and learning to identify negative thinking habits, clarifying the relationship between thoughts, feelings and behaviors and what is accurate or inaccurate about one's beliefs. Learning about cognitive distortions includes understanding false interpretation of cues, magnifying gambling skills, superstitions, illusion of control, selective memory, understanding of randomness and probability; identifying how falsely money and gambling are linked to self-esteem, social standing and power; cognitive restructuring directed toward the distorted thoughts, beliefs and attitudes about playing and winning games of chance; making better decisions concerning the struggles against impulsivity and urges; resolving difficulties with family members, and finding suitable solutions to gambling debts.

Psychosocial Educational groups address: addiction education, phases of pathological gambling, types of gambling behavior, and moods and cycles of gambling, self-defeating beliefs and boundaries issues.

Motivational Enhancement Strategies elicit and enhance clients' motivations to change their current destructive behaviors. These interventions also focus on the stages of change model that addresses intentional behavioral change, views change as a process rather that an event, recognizes the change process is characterized by a series of stages of change and explains that in attempting to change behavior clients typically cycle through these stages. The goals of these techniques include helping clients explore their present and potential problematic behaviors, helping the clients decide whether these behaviors are worth the costs and laying the groundwork for continuing ongoing change. These approaches are done in such a way that clients realize that all change is hard and that they can see their resistance and ambivalence to change and can experience their own need to change. This intervention helps develop the motivations to change and requires the clients to recognize and develop a discrepancy between who they currently are and who they wish to become. It allows the clients to process both cognitive and behavioral changes. This occurs in an atmosphere of acceptance. Rolling with resistance from the client is encouraged. Positive self-efficacy is an indicator of continued and future success. Goal setting and future positive aspirations are crucial for successful adaptive functioning in staying free of the destructive gambling cycle.

Family Therapy addresses the effects of compulsive gambling on the spouse and family members, family roles and expectations, financial difficulties, support for family members bearing the brunt of the pain, addressing the financial misery that accompanies the gambling addiction, providing guidance concerning family assets and dealing with the drained family finances. Families can help motivate clients and reduce relapse and dropouts from treatment. Family members can learn how to stop the enabling process and put limits on their own and the gambler's behaviors. Family members are able to learn about Gam-Anon and co-dependency.

Video Therapy uses movies and videos to deal with issues of denial, gambling addiction, making changes and the recovery process. The failure of breaking through the wall of denial is one of the major causes of relapse. By watching videos with specific pre-chosen themes clients can make their own choices as to how to make changes in their lives by watching the mistakes of others. Clients are able to see what the gambling addiction really looks like by observing actors playing roles making their mistakes obvious. By watching the mistakes of others motivation to change grows. Clients can see mistakes more clearly when it is acted out on video than they can by reading about it in a book or listening to a counselor try to explain it to them. There is a healing process in watching videos. Clients are able to gain insight by seeing themselves in the characters portrayed in a story that appears right before their eyes. It is a useful way of having clients come to their own insights without a figurehead leader of the group. Clients realize they are not alone, and knowing one is not alone is another important process in the healing process.

The **12-Step Gamblers Anonymous** program is a self-help, mutual support approach that focuses on keeping the pathological gambler from relapsing after they have gone through a state of awareness that the Intensive Outpatient Program provides. It fosters a unique fellowship that addresses gambling issues. It encourages gamblers to attend meetings where gamblers with similar problems can offer anonymity, support, understanding and education through fellowship, adherence to the 12-steps and sponsorship. This fellowship adheres to a spiritual program of growth, guided by the 12-step model of recovery that focuses on honesty, hope, faith, courage, integrity, willingness, humility, discipline, discretion, accountability, awareness and service. The process by which the GA program works is similar to a Gestalt approach in the healing power of presence in that members share their experience, strength, and hope by telling what they were like, what happened to change them and what they are doing now to keep from gambling.

The duration of a structured treatment program can extend from a brief intervention of a few minutes or hours to at least six to eight weeks and up to six months of group and individual counseling and GA attendance depending on the individual needs, life styles and life circumstances of each client. The groups generally meet for two hours. This includes family groups. Clients are encouraged to attend continuing care groups for the next six months of recovery after initial treatment. Attendance at Gamblers Anonymous while in treatment is strongly encouraged and clients are asked to attend three GA meetings each week. In all, between daily group sessions and GA meetings, clients could attend a recovery meeting every day of the week while in treatment. Daily therapy groups are designed to help interrupt the gambling behavior, as well as break through and understand a gambler's maladaptive patterns of behavior, breaking through the barriers of isolation and loneliness which maintain separateness from others. The program helps establish new communication patterns which will improve interpersonal relationships, identify and interpret destructive family and social relationships and replace these with constructive ways of thinking and new behaviors, and identify and encourage lifestyle changes necessary to maintain abstinence and recovery. The program also emphasizes identifying signals of relapse, discovering different ways of coping with feelings and provides and reinforces a strong continuing care program so that there is a foundation for the best possible support for continued abstinence and long-term recovery.

Treatment Program Evaluation

Evaluation of overall treatment program efficacy may be accomplished using client exit surveys, follow-up outcome data collection, or by using more comprehensive program evaluations such as the Gambling Treatment Outcome Monitoring System (GAMTOMS).

Profile of a Gambling Client

The gambler placed in a treatment program may have had no prior treatment or have an extensive treatment history; the client may be highly educated or have no education at all; they may have little or no work history or have had a long-term career or highly paid job; they may have inadequate anger management skills, act impulsively and be emotionally immature. There may be a criminal history and/or an antisocial behavioral value system. In other words, there is no stereotypical gambling client. The deciding factor for treatment placement is the severity of the client's disorder and the intensity of treatment and support needed to address the client's distress.

The Gambling Treatment Program

A treatment facility affords a haven wherein the gambler can face the problems and consequences of problem gambling safely, away from temptations and the stigma and anger of friends, family and employers.

Treatment approaches to pathological gambling include psychoanalytic, psychodynamic, behavioral, cognitive, pharmacological, addiction-based, multimodal, and self-help. A treatment program for pathological gamblers may use all of the approaches or any combination of the approaches. The National Institute on Drug Abuse (NIDA) has developed 13 "Principles of Effective Treatment" (NIDA, 1999). These principles also have broad application to the treatment of problem gambling. We support and encourage adherence to these 13 principles:

1. No single treatment is appropriate for all individuals.

2. Treatment needs to be readily available.

3. Effective treatment attends to multiple needs of the individual, not just his/her drug use.

4. An individual's treatment and services plan must be assessed continually and modified as necessary to ensure that the plan meets the person's changing needs.

5. Remaining in treatment for an adequate period of time is critical for treatment effectiveness.

6. Counseling (individual and/or group) and other behavioral therapies are critical components of effective treatment for addiction.

7. Medications are an important element of treatment for many patients, especially when combined with counseling and other therapies.

8. Addicted or drug-abusing individuals with coexisting mental disorders should have both disorders treated in an integrated way

9. Medical detoxification is only the first stage of addiction treatment and by itself does little to change long-term drug use.

10. Treatment does not need to be voluntary to be effective.

11. Possible drug use during treatment must be monitored continuously.

12. Treatment programs should provide assessment for HIV/AIDS, hepatitis B and C, tuberculosis, and other infectious diseases, and counseling to help patients modify or change behaviors that place themselves or others at risk of infection.

13. Recovery from drug addiction can be a long-term process and frequently requires multiple episodes of treatment.

More than two decades of scientific research have yielded this set of fundamental principles that characterize effective drug abuse treatment.

While some of the principles can be applied easily to gambling treatment, some may not. However, keeping the spirit of the principles to ensure stellar treatment is what is important. In addition, following the General Program Standards of the Commission on Accreditation of Rehabilitation Facilities (CARF), as outlined in their Behavioral Health Standards Manual, 2005 and 2009, would also add great validity to any program. Treatment programs may also wish to consider the Behavioral Health Care Elements of Performance specified by the Joint Commission on the Accreditation of Healthcare Organizations (JCAHO).

A comprehensive problem gambling treatment program can consist of up to twenty hours of gambling specific groups per week. This holds true for a stand-alone gambling program or a gambling program that is integrated into an alcohol and drug treatment program or any other addictions or mental health program.

Webster's New Encyclopedic Dictionary (1993 revision) defines program as "a plan of action." It is vital that a gambling program be truly a plan of action to treat problem and pathological gamblers. This is especially true if an agency is attempting to integrate gambling treatment into an existing treatment program for other types of addictions. Merely administering the screens and doing one or two groups does not constitute a program. Administering screenings and facilitating group sessions would be services your agency provides in support of the treatment program.

Spirituality is also an important component of the program. Individuals are encouraged to re-connect with their spirituality as they understand it. This component often gets lost when a gambler is in the midst of his/her addiction. Gamblers Anonymous groups should be readily available, both on and off site, if possible.

Groups may be one, two, three or more hours in duration depending on the structure of the treatment program. To supplement the core program, groups in art therapy, hiking, massage therapy, music, yoga, and other recreational programs may be added to enhance the program. It is important that the time spent in treatment be rich in activities that occupy the client to the extent that the preoccupation with gambling gets subsumed in the clinical, recreational and life-oriented activities enabling the client to concentrate on recovery.

VIII
Modules

The GPPC® Manual Module

Using the GPPC®

STEP 1: SCREENING

Screen the client using one or more of the screening tools included in the Screening and Assessment Instrument Module. The DSM-IV Criteria are used to determine the diagnosis for 312.31 Pathological Gambling. Five or more "Yes" answers on the DSM-IV, SOGS, or NODS suggests probable Pathological Gambling. Seven or more "Yes" answers on the GA 20 Questions suggests probable compulsive gambling. If the client has been screened within the last 30 days, go on to Step 2. If the client has never been screened, or not screened in the last 30 days, screen the client and continue.

STEP 2: FORMS TO USE

The GPPC Template (**Form #1, Manual Module**) provides the basic criteria for determining patient placement. Print out or copy this form as your worksheet. This form can be hand-written or typed. Refer to the Counselor Working Aid (**Form #2**) for prompts and sample questions for assessing severity in each dimension (D1–D6). Severity levels are listed on the GPPC **Form #3**. Severity ratings are assigned on a scale of 1 – 9, indicating a continuum from no significant symptoms (1) to extremely significant symptoms (9). Note that severity levels refer to the intensity of symptoms or the relative impediment to treatment in each dimension. Cumulative severity ratings in each dimension are used to determine the appropriate Level of Care (LOC) for the client. Suggested levels of care are listed on Levels of Care (GPPC **Form #4**). Examples of a completed GPPC are included as Example 1, Example 2, and Example 3 in the Completed Assessment Module.

STEP 3: FILLING IN THE GPPC HEADER INFORMATION

Client Name: Who is the client?

Gender: Client's self-identified gender

Last 5 SSN: Please provide the last 5 digits of the client's Social Security Number (SSN). This information is used only for research data filing and retrieval, not as client identifying information. If the client does not have a Social Security Number, use "00000."

DOB: The client's date of birth. Please use dd/mm/yyyy format (e.g., 11/30/1957).

Ethnicity: Client's self-reported racio-ethnic identification. This information is used only for research purposes.

IV Drug User: Prior or current intravenous drug use. This is used for research purposes and to prioritize patient placement.

Pregnant: Known or possible pregnancy. This is used for research purposes and to prioritize patient placement.

Nicotine: Prior or current use of tobacco products. This is used for research purposes and to determine possible additional health/treatment concerns.

Mil Vet: Prior or current military service. This is used for research purposes and to determine potential access to Veteran's Administration health care resources.

Employed: Is the client employed? This is used for research purposes and may be a factor in determining placement and level of care.

Marital Status: Prior/current marital status, e.g., single, married, married X2, divorced, divorced X2, separated.

Consents: Written consent by the client for the following purposes:

Treat: If the client has provided written consent to treatment. This information may also be specified in "Reports Made; Consents Given" below.

Release: If the client has provided written consent to release treatment information to designated individuals. This information may also be specified in "Reports Made; Consents Given" below.

Research: If the client has provided written consent to allow selected data to be used for research

---

purposes. This information may also specified in "Reports Made; Consents Given" below.

Evaluation Date: Date the evaluation was done. Please use dd/mm/yyyy format (e.g., 11/30/1957). This information is also used in "Additional Information" below.

Evaluation Location: Where the evaluation was done. (e.g., the office, agency, city or town where the evaluation was conducted). This information is also used in "Additional Information" below.

Initial GPPC: If this is the initial screening and placement determination.

Review GPPC: If this is a periodic review of Level of Care (LOC) or treatment progress, or if this is a change in LOC.

Discharge GPPC: If this is a completion of a particular LOC or completion of treatment.

Referral from: Source of referral (friend, treatment agency) or how the client came to find your agency (phone book, public service announcement).

Referral to: To whom will you subsequently refer the client for additional services. Expanded referral information may be included in "Referrals" below.

Mandated Tx: Is the client legally mandated for treatment?

Legal Eval Req: A separate legal evaluation may be required by various law enforcement and judicial systems.

Prior DSM: Give previous DSM-IV diagnostic codes, if any.

Prior LOC: Give previous Level of Care, if any.

Current DSM: Give current/provisional DSM-IV diagnostic codes based on current assessment.

Recommended LOC: Give recommended/provisional Level of Care based on current assessment.

STEP 4: FILLING IN THE GPPC DIMENSIONS

Use the Counselor Working Aid (**Form #2**) as a guide during the client interview. Fill in significant information in each of the six GPPC dimensions. If you need additional space, go to the GPPC Continuation Page, indicate the particular dimension, and continue. Use a numerical rating (1–9) in the box(es) to the right of a specific dimension. If this is an initial placement, use the Current Severity ("Cur") box. If this is a change in level of care, periodic reassessment or discharge, include both the prior severity rating ("Pri") and the current severity rating ("Cur"). Refer to the GPPC **Form #3** for numerical ratings of severity in each dimension.

STEP 5: ADDITIONAL HEADINGS/ CATEGORIES

Driving Dimensions: List the most significant prior/current dimension(s) for determining level of care and present clinical focus. This can guide the treatment plan. Re-evaluate as necessary as these driving dimensions may change over the course of treatment.

Suicidality; Threat to Self/Others: Use the "PLAID PALS" guidelines (Screening Instrument Module) to evaluate the severity or risk of Suicidal/Homicidal ideation, statement or plan. Suicidality is a significant risk factor for pathological gamblers.

Vulnerabilities/Strengths: List client's biopsychosocial strengths and weaknesses that contribute to client's ability to cope with demands of treatment and recovery (e.g., improving/deteriorating health or home environment).

Assessment Instruments Used and Results: List the assessment instruments used in the placement determination, the client's scores on the instruments, and the relative significance of these scores (e.g., "CLIENT answered "Yes" to 8 of 10 questions on the DSM-IV Gambling Screen, "Yes" to 12 of 17 questions on the NORC DSM-IV Screen for Gambling Problems (NODS), and "Yes" to 14 of 20 questions on the South Oaks Gambling Screen (SOGS). 5 or more "Yes" answers on any of the above instruments indicates probable Pathological Gambling. CLIENT answered "Yes" to 16 of 20 questions on the Gamblers Anonymous 20 Questions. 7 or more "Yes" answers on this survey suggest probable Compulsive Gambling.").

Clinical Impressions: Briefly recap the client's condition and provisional treatment recommendations. ("Client has a 15-year history of problem gambling with associated social, legal, and financial difficulty. Client is self-referred for treatment and appears to be in the Contemplation stage of change.") Include, as appropriate, Multiaxial diagnosis; Stage of Change; Basis for LOC recommendation; Appearance/hygiene; Presenting signs/symptoms; Mood/affect; Congruence/appropriateness of mood/affect; Speech rate/patterns; Behaviors during interview; Ability to read/complete intake paperwork; Degree of/ability to focus on/follow interview; Responsiveness

Reports Made; Consents Given: List any report or information provided as a result of the interview. Be sure to obtain client's written release. Indicate when and to whom the information was released (e.g., "At client request (with appropriate releases), copy of assessment with treatment recommendation to BFR Clinical Director and RPGC Clinical Director on 5/31/07.").

Provisional Treatment Plan & Discharge/Transition Criteria. Indicate an initial impression of needed level of care, time frame, any potential indicators of transition points in levels of care, and indicators of when the client might be discharged from treatment (success or failure) or transitioned into another level of care (progress or relapse/difficulty). (e.g., "Recommend LOC 2 (IOP) with GA meetings x3/weekly; consider for transition to Aftercare at six weeks; consider for discharge at end of 12 month Aftercare period based on successful progress.")

Disposition/Follow-up/Appointment/Re-interview: Indicate what happened as a result of the interview, whether a follow-up or re-interview is needed or was done, and any appointments made for the client (e.g., "CLIENT agreed to attend RPGC Orientation at 5:30pm Monday, June 4, and to begin IOP at that time. CLIENT also agreed to continue G.A. meeting attendance as part of the program.").

Referrals: Indicate to whom you refer the client, date, and point of contact.

Additional Information: Indicate the name of the individual performing the interview, the interviewer's credentials, the date and place of the interview (e.g., "Hugh DeMann, M.A., LADC, CPGC, performed this assessment on 5/31/07 at Reputable Counseling Services, LLP, Reno, NV 89502").

Counselor Signature/Title: Signature of the interviewer, credentials and date.

Supervisor Signature/Title: Signature of supervisor (if required), credentials and date.

STEP 6: A GPPC-BASED COMPREHENSIVE NARRATIVE ASSESSMENT

A GPPC-based client interview can also be used as the basis for a comprehensive narrative assessment. A sample of a Completed Assessment (**Example #2**) is provided as a reference.

CONFIDENTIAL

GAMBLING PATIENT PLACEMENT CRITERIA (GPPC®)

CLIENT NAME: **Gender:**
Last 5 SSN: **DOB:**   **Ethnicity:**
IV Drug User: ☐   **Pregnant:** ☐   **Nicotine:** ☐
Mil Vet: ☐   **Employed:** ☐   **Marital Status:**
CONSENT TO: Treat: ☐   **Release:** ☐   **Research:** ☐
Evaluation Date: **Evaluation Location:**
Initial GPPC: ☐   **Review GPPC:** ☐   **Discharge GPPC:** ☐
Referral from: **Referral to:**
Mandated Tx: ☐   **Legal Eval Required:** ☐
Prior DSM: **Prior LOC:**
Current DSM: **Recommended LOC:**

Prior/Current Level of Severity or Intensity of Treatment Indicated: - - - - - - - - - ->
Ratings: 1-3 – Low; 4-6 – Moderate; 7-9 – High (*Based on impediment to treatment, or severity*)

	Pri	Cur
D1) FREQUENCY/INTENSITY/DURATION OF DISORDER		
D2) BIOMEDICAL CONDITIONS/COMPLICATIONS:		
D3) COGNITIVE/BEHAVIORAL/EMOTIONAL CONDITIONS:		
D4) READINESS TO CHANGE:		
D5) RELAPSE or CONTINUED PROBLEM HISTORY/POTENTIAL:		
D6) CURRENT RECOVERY/LIVING ENVIRONMENT:		
DRIVING DIMENSIONS:		
SUICIDALITY; THREAT TO SELF/OTHERS:		

VULNERABILITIES/STRENGTHS:

ASSESSMENT INSTRUMENTS USED AND RESULTS:

CLINICAL IMPRESSIONS:

REPORTS MADE; CONSENTS GIVEN:

CONFIDENTIAL
Page 1 of 2
Form 1 GPPC® Template (Adapted from ASAM PPC-2R, 2001)
©2010 The GPPC® Initiative. All rights reserved.

PROVISIONAL TREATMENT PLAN & DISCHARGE/TRANSITION CRITERIA

DISPOSITION/FOLLOW-UP/APPOINTMENT/RE-INTERVIEW:

REFERRALS:

ADDITIONAL INFORMATION;

COUNSELOR SIGNATURE/TITLE: **DATE:**

SUPERVISOR SIGNATURE/TITLE: **DATE:**

Form 1 GPPC® Template (Adapted from ASAM PPC-2R, 2001)

GAMBLING PATIENT PLACEMENT CRITERIA (GPPC®)

CLIENT NAME: Gender:

Last 5 SSN: DOB: Ethnicity:

IV Drug User: ☐   Pregnant: ☐   Nicotine: ☐

Mil Vet: ☐   Employed: ☐   Marital Status:

CONSENT TO: Treat: ☐   Release: ☐   Research: ☐

Evaluation Date: Evaluation Location:

Initial GPPC: ☐   Review GPPC: ☐   Discharge GPPC: ☐

Referral from: Referral to:

Mandated Tx: ☐   Legal Eval Required: ☐

Prior DSM: Prior LOC:

Current DSM: Recommended LOC:

Prior/Current Level of Severity or Intensity of Treatment Indicated: - - - - - - - - - - >

Ratings: 1-3 – Low; 4-6 – Moderate; 7-9 – High (*Based on impediment to treatment, or severity*)

	Pri	Cur

D1) FREQUENCY/INTENSITY/DURATION OF DISORDER

_____
_____
_____
_____
_____
_____
_____

D2) BIOMEDICAL CONDITIONS/COMPLICATIONS:

_____
_____
_____
_____
_____
_____
_____

D3) COGNITIVE/BEHAVIORAL/EMOTIONAL CONDITIONS:

_____
_____
_____
_____
_____
_____
_____
_____

Form 1 GPPC® Template (Adapted from ASAM PPC-2R, 2001)

	Pri	Cur

D4) READINESS TO CHANGE:
_____
_____
_____
_____
_____
_____

D5) RELAPSE OR CONTINUED PROBLEM HISTORY/POTENTIAL:
_____
_____
_____
_____
_____
_____

D6) CURRENT RECOVERY/LIVING ENVIRONMENT:
_____
_____
_____
_____
_____
_____

DRIVING DIMENSIONS:
_____
_____
_____
_____
_____
_____

SUICIDALITY; THREAT TO SELF/OTHERS:
_____
_____
_____
_____
_____
_____

VULNERABILITIES/STRENGTHS:

_____
_____
_____
_____
_____
_____

ASSESSMENT INSTRUMENTS USED AND RESULTS:

_____
_____
_____
_____
_____
_____

CLINICAL IMPRESSIONS:

_____
_____
_____
_____
_____
_____

REPORTS MADE; CONSENTS GIVEN:

_____
_____
_____
_____
_____
_____

PROVISIONAL TREATMENT PLAN & DISCHARGE/TRANSITION CRITERIA:

_____
_____
_____
_____
_____
_____

Form 1 GPPC® Template (Adapted from ASAM PPC-2R, 2001)

DISPOSITION/FOLLOW-UP/RE-INTERVIEW:

_____

_____

_____

_____

_____

_____

REFERRALS:

_____

_____

_____

_____

_____

_____

ADDITIONAL INFORMATION:

_____

_____

_____

_____

_____

_____

COUNSELOR SIGNATURE/TITLE: _____ **DATE:** _____

SUPERVISOR SIGNATURE/TITLE: _____ **DATE:** _____

GPPC Continuation Page

_____
_____
_____
_____
_____
_____
_____
_____
_____
_____
_____
_____
_____
_____
_____
_____
_____
_____
_____
_____
_____
_____
_____
_____
_____
_____
_____
_____
_____
_____
_____
_____
_____
_____
_____
_____
_____
_____

Form 1 GPPC® Template (Adapted from ASAM PPC-2R, 2001)

GAMBLING PATIENT PLACEMENT CRITERIA (GPPC®)

CLIENT NAME: **Gender:**
Last 5 SSN: **DOB:**   **Ethnicity:**

IV Drug User: ☐   **Pregnant:** ☐   **Nicotine:** ☐

Mil Vet: ☐   **Employed:** ☐   **Marital Status:**

CONSENT TO: Treat: ☐   **Release:** ☐   **Research:** ☐

Evaluation Date: **Evaluation Location:**

Initial GPPC: ☐   **Review GPPC:** ☐   **Discharge GPPC:** ☐

Referral from: **Referral to:**

Mandated Tx: ☐   **Legal Eval Required:** ☐

Prior DSM: **Prior LOC:**

Current DSM: **Recommended LOC:**

Prior/Current Level of Severity or Intensity of Treatment Indicated: - - - - - - - - - ->
Ratings: 1-3 – Low; 4-6 – Moderate; 7-9 – High (*Based on impediment to treatment, or severity*)

Pri   Cur

D1) FREQUENCY/INTENSITY/DURATION OF DISORDER

DRIFT(Duration/Recurrence/Intensity/Financial Impact/Type) Date/Amount last gambled; Co-occurring/Concurrent disorder; ATOD use; Big Win/Loss;

D   Duration—Age first gambled or length of gambling behaviors
R   Recurrence—Pattern/frequency of gambling behaviors
I   Intensity—How much (time/money), first Big Win/Big Loss
F   Financial Impact or pressures
T   Type of gambling preferred

Additional presenting signs/symptoms or reported withdrawal symptoms (e.g., Irritability, Impatience, Restlessness, Jitteriness, Tremors, Sweating, Tension, Hyperactivity, Agitation, Dysphoria, Intense Craving, Anxiety, Depression, Inability to Concentrate, Headaches, Nausea, Sleep Disorders, Gastrointestinal Disorders, Other Disorders)

D2) BIOMEDICAL CONDITIONS/COMPLICATIONS:

Prior/Current Dx/Tx(Compliant with Tx?); Prior/Current Meds(Compliant with Meds?); Vegetative symptoms; Prior/current accident/injury/surgery; History of head trauma; Access to care
Does client appear medically stable?
Describe physical appearance; Medical or health conditions which may influence ability to participate in treatment; Medical conditions caused by or exacerbated by gambling; Any known allergies; Prior/current medications (Rx/OTC); Name of treatment provider.
Vegetative Symptoms (**SAWES**) – Recent change in **S**leep pattern, **A**ppetite, **W**eight, diurnal (daily) pattern of **E**nergy/mood, **S**ex drive (Reconsider/refer in Dimension 3)

D3) COGNITIVE/BEHAVIORAL/EMOTIONAL CONDITIONS:

Family of Origin; Upbringing; History of Individual/Family Substance-related or Behavioral addictions; History of Individual/Family Medical/Mental Health Dx/Tx(Compliant?); History of Individual/Family ATOD use; History of Individual/Family Medical/Mental Health Meds(Compliant?); History of Individual/Family Verbal/Emotional/Physical/Sexual(VEPS) abuse; History of Individual/Family Domestic Violence; History of Individual/Family Significant Losses (death/divorce/job/home); History of Suicidal Ideation/Attempt and/or family history of suicide/attempt; threat potential to self/others; History of juvenile/adult arrests/charges/incarceration;

> Any mental health disorders? Describe how the condition(s) manifests itself; Diagnosed by_____; Medications prescribed; Are medications being taken as directed?
>
> Is client on probation or parole? Name of officer/agency
>
> What is client's criminal history (include number of arrests, charges, convictions). Which occurred as a juvenile, as an adult?
>
> Discuss family of origin, education/training, employment history, military service
>
> Has a client been a victim of any abuse? If so list: Type, When, Perpetrator, Was this reported?, Outcome of report, Is the client currently at risk?
>
> Is Child Protective Services involved with the client?
>
> List all current stressors

D4) READINESS TO CHANGE:

Internal/external motivation to change/sustain; awareness of harmful effects; goals; self-help

> What is client's mood/affect when talking about treatment?
>
> AOD/Behavioral linkage to intended change
>
> Why does client think they are here, specifically?
>
> List motivational factors to complete treatment
>
> Discuss history of change, how does client react to it?
>
> What is client's knowledge of the effects of gambling on self?
>
> How long has the client been able to be gambling free?
>
> Prior treatment – when/where (include LOC's).
>
> Does client appear to focus on external or internal influences?
>
> "What would be the best thing about stopping your gambling today?"

STAGE OF CHANGE _____

D5) RELAPSE or CONTINUED PROBLEM HISTORY/POTENTIAL:

Progression; Prior/current ATOD/Behavioral abstinence/relapse; Pressing events; Triggers; Relapse prevention skills/experience; Intervention needs

> Primary game of choice; Age first played; Where first played; With whom played
>
> Pattern of gambling behaviors (frequency, intensity, duration)
>
> What other games has client played historically?
>
> What are client's thoughts and feelings about discontinuing gambling?

Form 2 GPPC® Counselor Working Aid (Adapted from ASAM PPC-2R, 2001)

How available are gambling venues?
Has the client overdrawn his bank accounts?
Has the client been preoccupied with gambling?
Has the client gambled with increasing amounts of money?
Has the client had unsuccessful attempts at cutting back or quitting?
Does the client return another day to recoup prior losses?
Does the client have access to the family finances?
Is there a family history of gambling?
What are client's triggers?
Has the client had prior treatment for gambling? Where? How long? What level of care?

D6) CURRENT RECOVERY/LIVING ENVIRONMENT: ▢▢

Current Employment/Housing/Transportation/Legal status; Current Cohabitants/Family/Friends/Social constellation/Support system; Current ATOD/Behavioral environment

Discuss current family/social situation. Include first names of relatives, where they reside.
What is the current status of the relationships? (Parents/Siblings/Cohabitants/Significant others/Children) List any other current significant relationships the client has.
List all family members who currently gamble; were they role models for the client? (Additional current ATOD/Behavioral addictions issues in family/social environment)
Does the client have a current formal living environment? (Adequate? Safe?)
Is the client currently employed?
How do the above factors influence the stability/likelihood of recovery?

DRIVING DIMENSIONS: ▢▢

For this phase of treatment; remarkable presentation; area of treatment focus

SUICIDALITY; THREAT TO SELF/OTHERS: ▢▢

Ideation/statement/attempt, inhibitors, PLAID PALS Screen indications

Consider including Risk Ratings (R0-R4) such as these adapted from ASAM PPC-2R:
R0 – The patient has good impulse control and coping skills
R1 – The patient has adequate impulse control and coping skills to deal with any thoughts of harm to self or others
R2 – The patient has suicidal ideation or violent impulses (but without active behaviors or intent), which require more than routine outpatient monitoring
R3 – The patient has frequent impulses to harm self or others, which are potentially destabilizing or chronic. However, the patient is not imminently dangerous in a 24-hour setting. For example, the patient has frequent suicidal ideation, but no plan and can contract for safety at Level III.
R4 – Severe psychotic, mood or personality disorders present acute risk to the patient, such as immediate risk of suicide, psychosis with unpredictable, disorganized or violent behavior, or gross neglect of self-care

Form 2 GPPC® Counselor Working Aid (Adapted from ASAM PPC-2R, 2001)

VULNERABILITIES/STRENGTHS:
Risk and Protective factors, Pending arrest/eviction/repossession, threats, destabilizing factors; spirituality, support groups, other counseling; self/mutual-help initiatives

ASSESSMENT INSTRUMENTS USED AND RESULTS:
Prior/recent instruments used to determine/adjust diagnosis or LOC

CLINICAL IMPRESSIONS:
Multiaxial diagnosis; Stage of Change; Basis for LOC recommendations; Appearance/hygiene; Presenting signs/symptoms; Mood/affect; Congruence/appropriateness of mood/affect; Speech rate/patterns; Behaviors during interview; Ability to read/complete intake paperwork; Degree of/ability to focus on/follow interview; Responsiveness

REPORTS MADE; CONSENTS GIVEN:
External reports requested/required; Point of contact; Client release required

PROFISIONAL TREATMENT PLAN & DISCHARGE/TRANSITION CRITERIA:
Recommended treatment approach; goals at each LOC; transition to subsequent LOC; aftercare

DISPOSITION/FOLLOW-UP/APPOINTMENT/RE-INTERVIEW:
Determination and disposition of report; follow-up required/made; next scheduled appointment; Continuation or re-interview required

REFERRALS:
Referral source for the client (self, counselor or agency, legal system) and any referrals to/of the client as part of this evaluation.

ADDITIONAL INFORMATION:
Interviewer identification/credentials; date/location of interview

COUNSELOR SIGNATURE/TITLE: _____ **DATE:** _____
SUPERVISOR SIGNATURE/TITLE: *(if required)* _____ **DATE:** _____

Form 2 GPPC® Counselor Working Aid (Adapted from ASAM PPC-2R, 2001)

GPPC® Form 3
Levels of Severity

Prior/Current Indicated Intensity of Treatment or Level of Severity Scale

9

8 – High — Significant danger/harm; Significant interference with daily living; Loss of resources; Chronic or persistent problems; High level of treatment needed

7

6

5 – Moderate — Moderate symptoms/problems/difficulties in social, occupational or home life. Transient or limited problems; Moderate level of treatment needed

4

3

2 – Low — Superior or satisfactory functioning. Absence or no report of significant symptoms/problems/difficulties; Minimal treatment/intervention needed

1

Impediment to Treatment or Levels of Severity

Numerical ratings applied to GPPC dimensions are used to quantify, in a relative way, the intensity of treatment required, any impediment to treatment, or the relative level of symptom severity, of the dimension being described. By listing Prior and Current levels, where available, the progress or change in condition of the client can be evaluated.

The GPPC is designed to be a living document and information resource for the practitioner. As such, the symptom severity levels assigned to the dimensions reflect to what degree the presenting problem will present an impediment or complication during a particular phase of treatment, as well as the intensity of treatment needed. For example, a client with severe Biomedical Conditions/Complications (Dimension 2) would generally be rated HIGH (somewhere between 7–9) in this dimension, not specifically because the medical conditions themselves are severe, but because they likely will present severe complications to satisfactory treatment and progress at a particular level of care.

The distinction between severity of the symptoms themselves and the degree of complication or impediment during treatment is particularly critical when evaluating Readiness to Change (Dimension 4). A client who is ready and willing to change problematic thinking and/or behaviors should generally be rated LOW (somewhere between 1–3), not because the client's motivation is low, but because the client's positive motivation will present a low impediment or complication to treatment at a particular level of care. Conversely, a client who is highly resistant or unwilling to change problematic thinking and/or behaviors should generally be rated HIGH (somewhere between 7–9), since this will be a significant impediment or complication to satisfactory treatment and progress at a particular level of care.

As another example, a client who returns to, or will return to, a safe and supportive Current Recovery/Living Environment (Dimension 6), should generally be rated LOW (somewhere between 1–3), since this positive environment will likely foster the client's progress during and after treatment. On the other hand, a homeless, unemployed client or a client returning to a hostile, threatening or unstable Recovery/Living environment should generally be rated HIGH (somewhere between 7–9) in this dimension, since this high-risk environment can significantly impede or complicate the client's satisfactory progress in treatment and recovery.

In the case of rating Suicidality; Threat to Self/Others, the utility of considering impediment or complication in treatment may be more intuitively obvious. A client at low risk of suicidal ideation or behavior and at low risk of harm to self or others should generally be rated LOW (somewhere between 1–3), since this will ordinarily not complicate treatment or recovery. A client with active suicidal ideation, threats or gestures, or with stated intent to harm self or others should be evaluated HIGH (somewhere between 7–9) since this not only impedes and/or complicates treatment and/or recovery, but indeed threatens the life of the client.

In general, then, the severity levels of the GPPC reflect the "degree of difficulty" the client and practitioner will face, based on one or more dimensional criteria, at a particular level of care. This rating is, of course, more than the best guess of the evaluator or practitioner, but is the rare combination of science and art, the objective documenting of the client's presenting problems and self-report blended and tempered with the considered clinical judgment of the skilled and experienced practitioner.

This rating system can be used to derive general guidelines for estimating or determining required level of care. As a general rule, a client with no dimensions rated MODERATE or HIGH can be expected to make satisfactory progress and recovery at a lower level of care than a client with multiple dimensions rated MODERATE and/or HIGH. A client with three or more dimensions rated HIGH, for example, can be expected to require treatment and care at the residential or inpatient level. A client whose dimensions begin to transition from a HIGH level to a MODERATE or LOW level during treatment can be expected to make satisfactory progress and recovery while transitioning to a lower level of care. Conversely, a client whose dimensions begin to move from LOW to MODERATE or HIGH during treatment may require additional focus at the current level of care or transition to a higher, more intensive level of treatment.

GPPC® Form 4
Levels of Care

Level 0.5   Early Intervention Services

Brief Intervention Services, Outreach, or Psychoeducational Groups for those with early stage problem gambling.

Level 1   Outpatient Services

Individual counseling, Case Management, Couple's Counseling, Family Counseling, Group Counseling, in a combination of services at the outpatient level, up to 7 hours per week.

Level 2   Intensive Outpatient Program Services

A specific program of outpatient treatment services (which may include individual, couple, family, group counseling and psychoeducation) specifically designed for pathological gambling provided by certified gambling treatment professionals, at a suggested minimum of 8 hours per week.

Level 3   Residential Treatment Services

Treatment within a building where the client resides and receives individual, group, case management, family, and/or couples counseling and other psycho-educational services until professionally assessed to be ready to move to a lower level of care or aftercare, at a suggested minimum of 20 hours per week

Continuing Care and Post-Treatment Services

Following successful completion of a recommended level of treatment such as IOP or Residential Treatment, extended and maintained contact between the treatment provider and the client, which may include a weekly group of alumni at a treatment center facilitated by a therapist.

> *Disclaimer: Any suggested lengths of treatment are not prescribed as written here, but rather reflect common time frames. The length of treatment is always a case-by-case decision by the treatment provider or treatment team and may have various ranges according to the facility.*

Screening and Assessment Instruments Module

Assessment Instrument Threshold
Levels and Terminology

DSM-IV

Answering "Yes" to five or more questions on this instrument meets diagnostic criteria for 312.31 Pathological Gambling

GA 20 Questions

"Most compulsive gamblers will answer 'Yes' to at least seven of these questions."

NODS (lifetime)

Answering "Yes" to one or two items on this instrument indicates an "at-risk gambler." Answering "Yes" to three or four items on this instrument indicates a "problem gambler." Answering "Yes" to five to ten items on this instrument indicates a "pathological gambler."

SOGS (lifetime)

Answering "Yes" to one to four items on this instrument indicates "some problems with gambling." Answering "Yes" to five or more items on this instrument indicates "probable pathological gambling."

DSM-IV Diagnostic Criteria

YES   **NO**

☐   ☐   1. Are you preoccupied with gambling (e.g. preoccupied with reliving past gambling experiences, handicapping, or planning your next gambling venture, or thinking of ways to get money for gambling?

☐   ☐   2. Do you need to gamble with increasing amounts of money in order to achieve your desired excitement?

☐   ☐   3. Have you had repeated unsuccessful efforts to control, cut back or stop gambling?

☐   ☐   4. Are you restless or irritable when attempting to cut back or stop gambling?

☐   ☐   5. Do you gamble as a way of escaping from problems or of relieving a dysphoric mood (e.g. feelings of helplessness, guilt, anxiety, depression)?

☐   ☐   6. After losing money gambling, do you often return another day to get even ("chasing" your losses)?

☐   ☐   7. Do you lie to family members, therapists or others to conceal the extent of your involvement with gambling?

☐   ☐   8. Have you committed illegal acts such as forgery, fraud, theft or embezzlement to finance your gambling?

☐   ☐   9. Have you jeopardized or lost a significant relationship, job or educational or career opportunity because of gambling?

☐   ☐   10. Do you rely on others to provide money to relieve a desperate financial situation caused by gambling?

Reprinted with permission from the *Diagnostic and Statistical Manual of Mental Disorders, Text Revised, Fourth Edition* (copyright 2000). American Psychiatric Association.

Gamblers Anonymous 20 Questions

Gamblers Anonymous offers the following questions to anyone who may have a gambling problem. These questions are provided to help the individual decide if he or she is a compulsive gambler and wants to stop gambling.

TWENTY QUESTIONS

1. Did you ever lose time from work or school due to gambling?

2. Has gambling ever made your home life unhappy?

3. Did gambling affect your reputation?

4. Have you ever felt remorse after gambling?

5. Did you ever gamble to get money with which to pay debts or otherwise solve financial difficulties?

6. Did gambling cause a decrease in your ambition or efficiency?

7. After losing did you feel you must return as soon as possible and win back your losses?

8. After a win did you have a strong urge to return and win more?

9. Did you often gamble until your last dollar was gone?

10. Did you ever borrow to finance your gambling?

11. Have you ever sold anything to finance gambling?

12. Were you reluctant to use "gambling money" for normal expenditures?

13. Did gambling make you careless of the welfare of yourself or your family?

14. Did you ever gamble longer than you had planned?

15. Have you ever gambled to escape worry, trouble, boredom or loneliness?

16. Have you ever committed, or considered committing, an illegal act to finance gambling?

17. Did gambling cause you to have difficulty in sleeping?

18. Do arguments, disappointments or frustrations create within you an urge to gamble?

19. Did you ever have an urge to celebrate any good fortune by a few hours of gambling?

20. Have you ever considered self destruction or suicide as a result of your gambling?

Most compulsive gamblers will answer yes to at least seven of these questions.

Used with permission of Gamblers Anonymous (2010)

NORC DSM-IV Screen for Gambling Problems (NODS)

(Please indicate Yes or No for behavior in the past year)

YES   **NO**

☐   ☐   1.   Have there ever been periods lasting 2 weeks or longer when you spent a lot of time thinking about your gambling experiences or planning out future gambling ventures or bets?

☐   ☐   2.   Have there ever been periods lasting 2 weeks or longer when you spent a lot of time thinking about ways of getting money to gamble with?

☐   ☐   3.   Have there ever been periods when you needed to gamble with increasing amounts of money or with larger bets than before in order to get the same feeling of excitement?

☐   ☐   4.   Have you ever tried to stop, cut down, or control your gambling?

☐   ☐   5.   On one or more of the times when you tried to stop, cut down, or control your gambling, were you restless or irritable?

☐   ☐   6.   Have you ever tried but not succeeded in stopping, cutting down, or controlling your gambling?

☐   ☐   7.   If so, has this happened 3 or more times?

☐   ☐   8.   Have you ever gambled as a way to escape from personal problems?

☐   ☐   9.   Have you ever gambled to relieve uncomfortable feelings such as guilt, anxiety, helplessness, or depression?

☐   ☐   10.   Has there ever been a period when, if you lost money gambling one day, you would return another day to get even?

☐   ☐   11.   Have you ever lied to family members, friends, or others about how much you gamble or how much money you lost on gambling?

☐   ☐   12.   If so, has this happened 3 or more times?

☐   ☐   13.   Have you ever written a bad check or taken money that didn't belong to you from family members or anyone else in order to pay for your gambling?

☐   ☐   14.   Has your gambling ever caused serious or repeated problems in your relationships with any of your family members or friends?

☐   ☐   15.   *Answer only if you are in school:* Has your gambling caused you any problems in school, such as missing classes or days of school or your grades dropping?

☐   ☐   16.   Has your gambling ever caused you to lose a job, have trouble with a job, or miss out on an important job or career opportunity?

☐   ☐   17.   Have you ever needed to ask family members or anyone else to loan you money or otherwise bail you out of a desperate money situation that was largely caused by your gambling?

Adapted from NORC DSM-IV Screen

NORC DSM-IV Screen for Gambling Problems

The screen is set up to run first a lifetime screen for all items and then ask about the past year only for those items endorsed for lifetime.

How to score the items:

Add 1 point for every YES to any of the following items:
1 or 2, 3, 5, 7, 8 or 9, 10, 12, 13, 14 or 15 or 16, 17

If gambler responds YES to more than one item in a response cluster (e.g., "8 or 9"), count them together as a single point.

Under the NODS typology

NODS

Answering "Yes" to one or two items on this instrument indicates an "at-risk gambler."
Answering "Yes" to three or four items on this instrument indicates a "problem gambler."
Answering "Yes" to five to ten items on this instrument indicates a "pathological gambler."

Adapted from The National Opinion Research Center (NORC) DSM-IV Screen for Gambling Problems.

Gerstein, Dean., S. Murphy, M. Toce, R. Volberg, et al. (1999). *Gambling Impact and Behavior Study: Report to the National Gambling Impact Study Commission.* Chicago: National Opinion Research Center (NORC) at the University of Chicago. http:www2.norc.org/new/gamb-fin.htm

South Oaks Gambling Screen (SOGS)

1. Indicate which of the following types of gambling you have done in your lifetime. For each type, mark one answer: "not at all," "less than once a week," or "once a week or more."

Not at all	Less than once a week	Once a week or more	
			a. played cards for money
			b. bet on horses, dogs or other animals (in off-track betting, at the track or with a bookie)
			c. bet on sports (parley cards, with a bookie, or at jai alai)
			d. played dice games (including craps, over and under, or other dice games) for money
			e. went to casino (legal or otherwise)
			f. played the numbers or bet on lotteries
			g. played bingo
			h. played the stock and/or commodities market
			i. played slot machines, poker machines or other gambling machines
			j. bowled, shot pool, played golf or played some other game of skill for money

2. What is the largest amount of money you have ever gambled with on any one day?

___ Never have gambled

___ $1.00 or less

___ More than $1 up to $10

___ More than $10 up to $100

___ More than $100 up to $1,000

___ More than $1,000 up to $10,000

___ More than $10,000

3. Do (did) your parents have a gambling problem?

___ both my father and mother gamble (or gambled) too much

___ my father gambles (or gambled) too much

___ my mother gambles (or gambled) too much

___ neither gambles (or gambled) too much

4. When you gamble, how often do you go back another day to win back money you lost?

___ never

___ some of the time (less than half the time) I lost

___ most of the time I lost

___ every time I lost

5. Have you ever claimed to be winning money gambling but weren't really? In fact, you lost?

___ never (or never gamble)

___ yes, less than half the time I lost

___ yes, most of the time

6. Do you feel you have ever had a problem with gambling?

___ no

___ yes, in the past, but not now

___ yes

	Yes	No
7. Did you ever gamble more than you intended?	___	___
8. Have people criticized your gambling?	___	___
9. Have you ever felt guilty about the way you gamble or what happens when you gamble?	___	___
10. Have you ever felt like you would like to stop gambling but didn't think you could?	___	___
11. Have you ever hidden betting slips, lottery tickets, gambling money, or other signs of gambling from your spouse, children, or other important people in you life?	___	___
12. Have you ever argued with people you live with over how you handle money?	___	___
13. (If you answered "yes" to question 12): Have money arguments ever centered on your gambling?	___	___
14. Have you ever borrowed from someone and not paid them back as a result of your gambling?	___	___

15. Have you ever lost time from work (or school) due to gambling?   ____ ____

16. If you borrowed money to gamble or to pay gambling debts,
    where did you borrow from? (Check "yes" or "no" for each.)

        a. from household money   ____ ____

        b. from your spouse   ____ ____

        c. from other relatives or in-laws   ____ ____

        d. from banks, loan companies, or credit unions   ____ ____

        e. from credit cards   ____ ____

        f.   from loan sharks (Shylocks)   ____ ____

        g. your cashed in stocks, bonds or other securities   ____ ____

        h. you sold personal or family property   ____ ____

        i.   you borrowed on your checking account (passed bad   ____ ____
           checks)

        j.   you have (had) a credit line with a bookie   ____ ____

        k. you have (had) a credit line with a casino   ____ ____

Scoring Rules for SOGS

Scores are determined by adding up the number of questions that show an "at risk" response, indicated as follows. If you answer the questions above with one of the following answers, mark that in the space next to that question:

Questions 1-3 are not counted.

_____ Question 4: most of the time I lost, or every time I lost

_____ Question 5: yes, less than half the time I lose, or yes, most of the time

_____ Question 6: yes, in the past, but not now, or yes

_____ Question 7: yes

_____ Question 8: yes

_____ Question 9: yes

_____ Question 10: yes

_____ Question 11: yes

Question 12 is not counted.

_____ Question 13: yes

_____ Question 14: yes

_____ Question 15: yes

_____ Question 16a: yes

_____ Question 16b: yes

_____ Question 16c: yes

_____ Question 16d: yes

_____ Question 16e: yes

_____ Question 16f: yes

_____ Question 16g: yes

_____ Question 16h: yes

_____ Question 16i: yes

Questions 16j and 16k are not counted.

Total = _____ (20 questions are counted)

**1 to 4 = Some problems with gambling
**5 or more = Probable pathological gambler

Reprinted with permission from the American Journal of Psychiatry (copyright 1987). American Psychiatric Association.

NOTE: The authors' preferred approach to these scoring guidelines is more closely aligned with the NODS typology of: 1 or 2 = "at-risk gambler," 3 or 4 = "problem gambler," 5 or more = "pathological gambler."

P.L.A.I.D. P.A.L.S.

Things to watch for when assessing potential suicide risk...

Plan – Do they have one?

Lethality – Is it lethal? Can they die?

Availability – Do they have the means to carry it out?

Illness – Do they have a mental or physical illness?

Depression– Chronic or specific incident(s)?

Previous attempts – How many? How recent?

Alone – Are they alone? Do they have a support system? A partner?
Are they alone right now?

Loss– Have they suffered a loss? Death, job, relationship, self esteem?

Substance abuse (or use) – Drugs, alcohol, medicine? Current, chronic?

ASAM Risk Ratings:
Suicidality; Threat to Self/Others

Ideation/statement/attempt, inhibitors, PLAID PALS Screen indications

Consider including Risk Ratings (R0-R4) such as these adapted from ASAM PPC-2R:

R0 – The patient has good impulse control and coping skills

R1 – The patient has adequate impulse control and coping skills to deal with any thoughts of harm to self or others

R2 – The patient has suicidal ideation or violent impulses (but without active behaviors or intent), which require more than routine outpatient monitoring

R3 – The patient has frequent impulses to harm self or others, which are potentially destabilizing or chronic. However, the patient is not imminently dangerous in a 24-hour setting. For example, the patient has frequent suicidal ideation, but no plan and can contract for safety.

R4 – Severe psychotic, mood or personality disorders present acute risk to the patient, such as immediate risk of suicide, psychosis with unpredictable, disorganized or violent behavior, or gross neglect of self-care

Adapted from ASAM PPC-2R

The LIE/BET Questionnaire for Screening Pathological Gambling

Have you ever felt the need to bet more and more money?

Have you ever had to lie to people important to you about how much you gambled?

Johnson, E. E., R. Hamer, R. M. Nora, et al. (1997).
The lie/bet questionnaire for screening pathological gamblers.
Psychological Reports, 80, pp. 83–88.

Completed Assessments Module

EXAMPLE 1

GAMBLING PATIENT PLACEMENT CRITERIA (GPPC®)

CLIENT NAME:	Wanda Bigwynne			**Gender:**	F
Last 5 SSN: 22112		**DOB:**	2/14/48	**Ethnicity:**	Black
IV Drug User:	☐	**Pregnant:**	☐	**Nicotine:**	☒
Mil Vet:	☒	**Employed:**	☒	**Marital Status:**	D
CONSENT TO: Treat:	☒	**Release:**	☒	**Research:**	☒
Evaluation Date:	5/31/07	**Evaluation Location:**	RCS, Tonopah, NV		
Initial GPPC:	☒	**Review GPPC:**	☐	**Discharge GPPC:**	☐
Referral from: Self-referred		**Referral to:**	RPGC IOP		
Mandated Tx:	☐	**Legal Eval Required:**	☐		
Prior DSM:	311.00	**Prior LOC:**	None		
Current DSM: 312.31; 305.10		**Recommended LOC:**	Level 2 IOP		

Prior/Current Level of Severity or Intensity of Treatment Indicated: - - - - - - - - - ->
Ratings: 1-3 – Low; 4-6 – Moderate; 7-9 – High (*Based on impediment to treatment, or severity*)

Pri/Cur

D1) FREQUENCY/INTENSITY/DURATION OF DISORDER | 7 |

 No current signs/symptoms of acute intoxication/withdrawal or of active gambling
or withdrawal distress noted/reported. Client reports a 10-year history of increasingly problematic gambling
with related social, interpersonal and legal difficulty. Client reports first episode of gambling at age 50 after
coming to Nevada when she divorced. She reports her "big win" of $7,200 on a video poker machine within the
first year. Client now reports weekly episodes of uncontrolled gambling (on paydays) resulting in loss of entire
paycheck ($1,700). Client reports biggest one-time loss of $4,400 last year. Client is now delinquent in rent,
utilities, and car payment. Client reports prior withdrawal symptoms (when unable to gamble or during repeated
attempts to stop gambling) of irritability, impatience, restlessness, jitters, agitation, craving, dysphoria, poor
concentration, depression, tension and sleep disturbance. Client reports smoking up to one pack of cigarettes
daily since age 20, with similar withdrawal symptoms as noted above when attempting to quit smoking. Client
denies use of alcohol/drugs. Client denies history of seizures or manic episodes.

D2) BIOMEDICAL CONDITIONS/COMPLICATIONS: | 2 |

Client describes current overall emotional/physical condition as "good" and
"stable," and denies prior/current medical conditions/complications. Client denies prior/current dental problems,
denies prior/current biomedical or communicable disease issues, and denies prior/current medications other than
as prescribed (See Dimension 3 below). Client denies recent significant change in appetite/sleep patterns,
change in weight, change in diurnal patterns of energy/mood, or recent change in sex drive. Currently, her
eyes/skin are clear, she appears alert and coherent, her mood and affect are congruent and appropriate, and she
appears to be in relatively good physical condition. Client denies history of accident, serious injury, major
surgery, or head trauma. Client denies allergies. Client reports she has not requested or required medical
treatment recently, other than as described below (Dimension 3).

D3) COGNITIVE/BEHAVIORAL/EMOTIONAL CONDITIONS: | 6 |

Client reports current diagnosis/treatment for mental/emotional disorder, specifically, 311.00, Depressive Disorder NOS (VAMC, 2005), for which she continues to receive treatment at the local V.A. hospital. Treatment includes prescription Celexa® (citalopram) with satisfactory result. Client reports she was raised by her biological parents, who divorced when she was age 10. Client was subsequently raised by her father. Her father abused alcohol, but was abstinent for about 10 years before he died in 2005. Client reports two younger brothers, both of whom abuse alcohol. Client denies history of verbal/emotional/physical/sexual (VEPS) abuse while growing up. Client reports being married twice: first, from 1972-1974, and from 1975-1984, with two children (son age 29, daughter age 26) from her first marriage. Client denies history of mutual VEPS abuse with her husbands or children. Client denies prior/current involvement with CPS. Client reports daily stress concerning her financial problems. Client reports current adequate housing and is currently employed, but as noted above, is delinquent in all her bills. Client reports she completed 14 years of school with no additional vocational/technical training. Client is a military veteran. Client denies history of juvenile arrests/charges. Client reports adult arrests/charges for "bad checks." Client reports lifetime cumulative incarceration of one month. Client denies prior/current probation/parole.

D4) READINESS TO CHANGE: | 4 |

Client appears to have internal motivation for treatment, to change thinking/behaviors and to sustain those changes. "I want to become a better person, enjoy life and help others." Client appears to be concerned about her own welfare and future. Client appears to be aware of the harmful effects of gambling and tobacco use on her emotional, physical and mental health, legal problems, and overall well-being. Client states her life without gambling will be "better," although she will "miss" the socialization and excitement. Client appears sincere in her stated intent to change behaviors, but is aware it will be difficult and unfamiliar. Client reports her longest prior period of abstinence from gambling was approximately three weeks (current), and reports she was lonely and bored. Client denies attending self-help or mutual-support groups. Client appears to be in the Preparation stage of change per interview and self-report.

D5) RELAPSE or CONTINUED PROBLEM HISTORY/POTENTIAL: | 8 |

Client reports regular, progressively more severe episodes of gambling, and smokes heavily when she plays. Client reports numerous prior unsuccessful attempts to quit, control or moderate her gambling and smoking. Client reports her longest period of abstinence from gambling or smoking to be three weeks (current). Client reports preoccupation with gambling at the cause/solution of her financial problems. Client reports first gambling at age 50, and almost continually since, with last episode three weeks ago. Client reports gambling as often as daily since moving to Nevada. Client reports she began by playing cards (poker), but now prefers video slots and Keno. Current environment includes numerous 24-hour gaming venues. Client appears to have no effective relapse prevention knowledge/skills/experience, and remains quite vulnerable to relapse to gambling and smoking. In addition to pathological gambling and tobacco-cessation treatment, client would benefit from relapse prevention and sober living counseling.

D6) CURRENT RECOVERY/LIVING ENVIRONMENT: | 8 |

Client currently lives alone in adequate housing, but may face eviction for nonpayment of rent, and her car may be repossessed. She is currently employed. Client reports little, if any, stable, supportive social network beyond a neighbor and a friend at work. Client reports her family relationships (son, daughter and two brothers who abuse alcohol) have been strained by her geographic isolation and gambling behavior. She reports feeling so lonely at times that she goes to the casino to be with people. Client will benefit from assistance in developing social skills and a social support system.

DRIVING DIMENSIONS: | 1,3,5,6 |

Current driving dimensions are 1,3,5,6 based on intensity of gambling (DIM 1), mood disorder (DIM 3), relapse potential (DIM 5), and lack of social support (DIM 6).

Form 1 GPPC® Template (Adapted from ASAM PPC-2R, 2001)

SUICIDALITY; THREAT TO SELF/OTHERS: `[        2        ]`

Client denies prior/current suicidal ideation/plan/attempt and denies family history of suicide/attempt. Client currently appears to present a low risk (R1) of suicide, homicide, or threat to self or others.

VULNERABILITIES/STRENGTHS:

VULNERABILITIES: Client lacks stable social supports and lacks relapse prevention skills. Client facing possible eviction and repossession of car for payment arrears. STRENGTHS: Client appears to be willing to comply with treatment and appears to be concerned about her future, with internal motivation for treatment. Client appears to be in relatively good health. Client reports receiving employment income and continuing access to Veteran's Administration health care resources. Client appeared to be focused, responsive and cooperative throughout the interview.

ASSESSMENT INSTRUMENTS USED AND RESULTS:

Client answered "Yes" to 8/10 questions on the DSM Gambling Screen, "Yes" to 15/17 questions on the NORC DSM-IV Screen for Gambling Problems (NODS), and "Yes" to 15/20 questions on the South Oaks Gambling Screen (SOGS). 5 or more "Yes" answers on any of the above instruments indicates probable Pathological Gambling. CLIENT answered "Yes" to 16/20 questions on the Gamblers Anonymous 20 Questions. 7 or more "Yes" answers on this survey suggests probable Compulsive Gambling. The Substance Abuse Subtle Screening Inventory (SASSI) was not administered during this assessment.

CLINICAL IMPRESSIONS:

AXIS I:	312.31; 305.10 per self-report
AXIS II:	V71.09 No Diagnosis on Axis II
AXIS III:	311.00 prior Dx per self-report
AXIS IV:	Problems with primary support group, Economic problems
AXIS V:	GAF = 55 (current)

Client reports a 10 year history of gambling, with associated social, interpersonal and legal difficulty. Client appeared to be candid during the interview, and appears to be somewhat aware of the unsuccessful nature of her thinking and behavior patterns. Client appears to believe she can complete a treatment program as well as attain and maintain abstinence. Client presented promptly for the interview, with appropriate hygiene/grooming/attire, pleasant/congruent mood/affect and was courteous/cooperative/responsive. Client read all interview/assessment paperwork without difficulty, completed necessary paperwork, and appears willing to comply with treatment.

This client meets diagnostic criteria for Pathological Gambling, as evidenced by maladaptive gambling behavior as indicated by five (or more) of the following: preoccupation with gambling; need to gamble with increasing amounts; repeated unsuccessful efforts to control, cut back, or stop gambling; restlessness/irritability when attempting to cut down/stop gambling; gambling to escape from problems or relieve dysphoric mood; after losing, "chasing" losses; lying to others to conceal extent of involvement with gambling; committing illegal acts to finance gambling; jeopardized/lost relationship/job/educational or career opportunity because of gambling; or reliance on others to relieve desperate gambling-related financial situation.

This client appears to be in the Preparation stage of change based on self-report. Based on frequency/intensity/duration of disorder and the severity of Dimensions One/Three/Five/Six, this client would benefit from GPPC Level 2 (Intensive Outpatient) treatment and care for Pathological Gambling.

Form 1 GPPC® Template (Adapted from ASAM PPC-2R, 2001)

REPORTS MADE; CONSENTS GIVEN:
At client request (with appropriate releases), copy of assessment with treatment recommendation mailed to RPGC Clinical Director on 5/31/07.

PROVISIONAL TREATMENT PLAN & DISCHARGE/TRANSITION CRITERIA
Client to attend six weeks of Intensive Outpatient treatment for Pathological Gambling. Client to attend aftercare weekly for up to one year following successful completion of Outpatient treatment. Client to attend Gamblers Anonymous (GA) meetings at least three times weekly. Client to seek smoking-cessation treatment.

DISPOSITION/FOLLOW-UP/APPOINTMENT/RE-INTERVIEW:
Client agreed to attend RPGC Orientation at 5:30pm Monday, June 4, and to begin IOP at that time. Client also agreed to begin GA meeting attendance as part of the program.

REFERRALS:
Client referred to Butts-Out Counseling, Tonopah, NV for smoking-cessation services.

ADDITIONAL INFORMATION:
Hugh DeMann, M.A., LADC-S, CPGS-S, performed this assessment on 5/31/07 at Reputable Counseling Services, LLP, Tonopah, NV 89049.

COUNSELOR SIGNATURE/TITLE: /s/ High DeMann **DATE:** 5/31/07

SUPERVISOR SIGNATURE/TITLE: **DATE:**

EXAMPLE 2

GAMBLING PATIENT PLACEMENT CRITERIA (GPPC®)

CLIENT NAME **Wanda Bigwynne**   Gender: **F**
Last 5 SSN: **-22112**   DOB: **2/14/48**   Ethnicity: **Black**

IV Drug User: ☐   Pregnant: ☐   Nicotine: ☐
Mil Vet: ☑   Employed: ☐   Marital Status: **Div.**
CONSENT TO: Treat: ☑   Release: ☑   Research: ☑
Evaluation Date: **5/31/07**   Evaluation Location: **RCS, Tonopah**
Initial GPPC: ☑   Review GPPC: ☐   Discharge GPPC: ☐
Referral from: **self**   Referral to: **RPGC - IOP**
Mandated Tx: ☐   Legal Eval Required: ☐
Prior DSM: **311.00**   Prior LOC: **∅**
Current DSM: **312.31, 305.10**   Recommended LOC: **level 2 Intensive Outpatient**

Prior/Current Level of Severity: ->
Ratings: 1-3 – Low; 4-6 – Moderate; 7-9 – High (Based on impediment to treatment, or severity)

Pri/Cur

D1) FREQUENCY/INTENSITY/DURATION OF DISORDER   [ ] [7]

10-yr hx of p.g., first @ 50 yrs, following Reno visit when divorced. First big win: $7,200 – video poker, during 1st yr. gambling. Now gambles weekly, no control: losing entire paycheck ($1,700). Biggest 1-day loss = $4,400 – last year. Prior w/d symptoms w/ repeated attempts to stop. Smokes 1 pack cigarettes qd since '20. Denies AOD. Delinquent in bills.

D2) BIOMEDICAL CONDITIONS/COMPLICATIONS: [ ] [2]

Overall emotional/physical health = "good, stable." Denies prior complaints. ∅ dental; communicable diseases; denies Rx abuse or current need for Rx. Denies Δ in sleep, appetite, weight, energy or sex drive. Appears clear, alert, healthy; affect congruent with appearance. Denies hx of accident, injury, or surgery.

D3) COGNITIVE/BEHAVIORAL/EMOTIONAL CONDITIONS: [ ] [6]

Current dx 311.00 (depressive disorder NOS) being treated @ VAMC since 2005, including Rx of Celexa used satisfactorily. Bio-parents raised her; they div. when she was 10, then raised by Dad. Father died 2005. He abused ETOH, but was abstinent last 10 yrs. Two younger bros. abuse ETOH. Denies hx VEPS during marriages or in childhood. 2 marriages: 1972-1974; 1975-1984. 2 children (29 & 26) from 1st marriage. Housing okay except for delinquent bills. Completed 14 yrs school. Denies juv. arrest hx. (+) Arrests for bad checks (+) Military hx. Lifetime incarceration = 1 mo.

Page 1

Form 1 GPPC® Template (Adapted from ASAM PPC-2R, 2001)

©2010 The GPPC® Initiative. All rights reserved.

D4) READINESS TO CHANGE: | 4 |

Appears internally motivated. "I want to become a better person, enjoy life, and help others." ⊕ Concern about her own welfare and future! ⊕ Awareness of harmful effects of gambling and tobacco use. Says "life w/o gambling will be better," although she will "miss the socialization & excitement." Longest abstinence from gambling = 3 wks. Currently lonely & bored (during abstinence). Denies any self help/G.A. attendance.

D5) RELAPSE OR CONTINUED PROBLEM HISTORY/POTENTIAL: | 8 |

Regular, continuous gambling and no prior tx. Smoking ↑ when gambling, numerous prior unsuccessful attempts to quit gambling or smoking. Last episode 3 wks ago. Longest abstinence from gambling in 10 years = 3 wks (current 3 weeks before this eval.) Played daily since moving to Reno. Started w/ cards (poker) now prefers video slots and Keno. No effective relapse prevention knowledge/skills or experience: very vulnerable to relapse.

D6) CURRENT RECOVERY/LIVING ENVIRONMENT: | 8 |

Lives alone; housing adequate but may face eviction for non-payment of rent. ↓/⊖ stable supportive social network, other than 1 friend and 1 neighbor. Car may be repo'd. Currently unemployed. Family relations strained by distance and their disdain of her gambling and all she has borrowed. Loneliness preceeds her trips to casinos. Client will benefit from ↑ personal skills and ⊕ support system.

DRIVING DIMENSIONS: | 1, 3, 5, 6 |

1, 3, 5, 6 high, based on intensity of gambling, mood disorder, relapse potential and ↓ support system.

SUICIDALITY; THREAT TO SELF/OTHERS: | 2 |

Denies prior or current suicidal ideation, plan, or attempt. Denies family hx of suic/att. Currently appears low risk of harm to self or others.

VULNERABILITIES/STRENGTHS:

willing, voluntary, compliant, concerned, hopeful and internally motivated. Good health. Receives V.A. resources. Looking for work. Focused, responsive and cooperative.
Lacks soc. supports and treatment knowledge or relapse prevention skills. Housing, transportation and financial problems are extreme.

ASSESSMENT INSTRUMENTS USED AND RESULTS:

DSM IV = 8/10 yes, NODS: 15/17 yes; SOGS: 15/20 yes, GA 20 Q: 16/20 yes.

CLINICAL IMPRESSIONS:

Axis I: 312.31, 305.10
Axis II: V71.09 No dx
Axis III: 311.00
Axis IV: Problems w/ primary support; Economic probs.
Axis V: 55 (Current GAF)

REPORTS MADE; CONSENTS GIVEN:

With releases, client requests copy of GPPC w/ tx rec. to go to RPGC. Clinical Director to request IOP tx 5/31/07.

PROVISIONAL TREATMENT PLAN & DISCHARGE/TRANSITION CRITERIA:

✓ Recommend minimum 6 weeks IOP @ RPGC for pathological Gambling treatment; 1 year weekly continuing care group involvement following successful completion of level 2 IOP.
✓ GA 3x week indefinitely; obtain & use a sponsor & work the 12 steps of GA; seek a service position in GA. for & support and fellowship with recovering gamblers.
✓ Seek smoking cessation tx.
✓ Follow directions of 4/counselors in outpatient mental health care.

Form 1 GPPC® Template (Adapted from ASAM PPC-2R, 2001)

DISPOSITION/FOLLOW-UP/APPOINTMENT/RE-INTERVIEW:

Client agreed to attend RPGC orientation appt.
@ 5:30 pm Monday, 6/4/07 and immediately
begin level 2 IOP.
She also agreed to attend G.A. 5/31/07, with a
commitment to get a phone list and make daily
contact with recovering G.A. members, daily as of 5/31/07.

REFERRALS:

Referred to "Butts Out Counseling" smoking cessation program

ADDITIONAL INFORMATION:

Hugh DeMann, M.A., LADC-S, CPGC-S,
completed this GPPC 5/31/07 @ Reputable Counseling
Services (RPS) in Tonopah, NV.

COUNSELOR SIGNATURE/TITLE: _Hugh DeMann_   **DATE:** _5/31/07_

SUPERVISOR SIGNATURE/TITLE: _____   **DATE:** _____

Form 1 GPPC® Template (Adapted from ASAM PPC-2R, 2001)

EXAMPLE 3

GPPC® ASSESSMENT

Client Name: Wanda Bigwynne   **Gender:** Female

Last 5 SSN: 22112   **DOB:** 2/14/48   **Ethnicity**: Black

IV Drug User: No   **Pregnant:** No   **Nicotine**: Yes

Mil Vet: Yes   **Employed:** Yes   **Marital Status:** Divorced

Consents to: **Treat:** Yes   **Release:** Yes   **Research:** Yes

Evaluation Date: 5/31/07   **Evaluation Location**: RCS, Tonopah

Initial GPPC: Yes   **Review GPPC:** No   **Discharge GPPC:** No

Referral Source: Self-referred   **Referral to:** RPGC - IOP

Mandated Tx: No   **Legal Eval Req:** No

Prior DSM: 311.00   **Prior LOC:** None

Current DSM: 312.31 Pathological Gambling; 305.10 Nicotine Dependence per self-report

Recommended Level of Care: GPPC Level II Intensive Outpatient (IOP)

General Information: CLIENT is a 60-year-old divorced (twice-married) Black female with two children, self-referred for evaluation/treatment. Her stated reason for seeking evaluation/treatment at this time is, "I can't seem to stop gambling."

GPPC® DIMENSIONS

D1) Frequency/Intensity/Duration of Disorder: 7 (High)

No current signs/symptoms of acute intoxication/withdrawal or of active gambling or withdrawal distress noted/reported. CLIENT reports a 10 year history of increasingly problematic gambling with related social, interpersonal and legal difficulty. CLIENT reports first episode of gambling at age 50 after coming to Nevada when she divorced. She reports her "big win" of $7,200 on a video poker machine within the first year. CLIENT now reports weekly episodes of uncontrolled gambling (on paydays) resulting in loss of entire paycheck ($1,700). Client reports biggest one-time loss of $4,400 last year. CLIENT is now delinquent in rent, utilities, and car payment. CLIENT reports prior withdrawal symptoms (when unable to gamble or during repeated attempts to stop gambling) of irritability, impatience, restlessness, jitters, agitation, craving, dysphoria, poor concentration, depression, tension and sleep disturbance. Client reports smoking up to one pack of cigarettes daily since age 20, with similar withdrawal symptoms as noted above when attempting to quit smoking. CLIENT denies use of alcohol/ drugs. CLIENT denies history of seizures or manic episodes.

D2) Biomedical Conditions/Complications: 2 (Low)

CLIENT describes current overall emotional/physical condition as "good" and "stable," and denies prior/current medical conditions/complications. CLIENT denies prior/current dental problems, denies prior/current biomedical or communicable disease issues, and denies prior/current medications other than as prescribed (See Dimension 3 below). CLIENT denies recent significant change in appetite/sleep patterns, change in weight, change in diurnal patterns of energy/mood, or recent change in sex drive. Currently, her eyes/skin are clear, she appears alert and coherent, her mood and affect are congruent and appropriate, and she appears to be in relatively good physical condition. CLIENT denies history of accident, serious injury, major surgery, or head trauma. CLIENT denies allergies. CLIENT reports she has not requested or required medical treatment recently, other than as described below (Dimension 3).

D3) Cognitive/Behavioral/Emotional Conditions: 6 (Moderate)

CLIENT reports current diagnosis/treatment for mental/emotional disorder, specifically, 311.00, Depressive Disorder NOS (VAMC, 2005), for which she continues to receive treatment at the local V.A. hospital. Treatment includes prescription Celexa (citalopram) with satisfactory result. CLIENT reports she was raised by her biological parents, who divorced when she was age 10. CLIENT was subsequently raised by her father. Her father abused alcohol, but was abstinent for about 10 years before he died in 2005. CLIENT reports two younger brothers, both of whom abuse alcohol. CLIENT denies history of verbal/emotional/physical/sexual (VEPS) abuse while growing up. CLIENT reports being married twice: first, from 1972-1974, and from 1975-1984, with two children (son age 29, daughter age 26) from her first marriage. CLIENT denies history of mutual VEPS abuse with her husbands or children. CLIENT denies prior/current involvement with CPS. CLIENT reports daily stress concerning her financial problems. CLIENT reports current adequate housing and is currently employed, but as noted above, is delinquent in all her bills. CLIENT reports she completed 14 years of school with no additional vocational/technical training. CLIENT is a military veteran.

CLIENT denies history of juvenile arrests/charges. CLIENT reports adult arrests/charges for "bad checks." CLIENT reports lifetime cumulative incarceration of one month. CLIENT denies prior/current probation/parole.

D4) Readiness to Change: 4 (Moderate)

CLIENT appears to have internal motivation for treatment, to change thinking/behaviors and to sustain those changes. "I want to become a better person, enjoy life and help others." CLIENT appears to be concerned about her own welfare and future. CLIENT appears to be aware of the harmful effects of gambling and tobacco use on her emotional, physical and mental health, legal problems, and overall well-being. CLIENT states her life without gambling will be "better," although she will "miss" the socialization and excitement. CLIENT appears sincere in her stated intent to change behaviors, but is aware it will be difficult and unfamiliar. CLIENT reports her longest prior period of abstinence from gambling was approximately three weeks (current), and reports she was lonely and bored. CLIENT denies attending self-help or mutual-support groups. CLIENT appears to be in the Preparation stage of change per interview and self-report.

D5) Relapse or Continued Problem History/Potential: 8 (High)

CLIENT reports regular, progressively more severe episodes of gambling, and smokes heavily when she plays. CLIENT reports numerous prior unsuccessful attempts to quit, control or moderate her gambling and smoking. CLIENT reports her longest period of abstinence from gambling or smoking to be three weeks (current). CLIENT reports preoccupation with gambling as the cause/solution of her financial problems.

CLIENT reports first gambling at age 50, and almost continually since, with last episode three weeks ago. CLIENT reports gambling as often as daily since moving to Nevada. CLIENT reports she began by playing cards (poker), but now prefers video slots and Keno. Current environment includes numerous 24-hour gaming venues.

CLIENT appears to have no effective relapse prevention knowledge/skills/experience, and remains quite vulnerable to relapse to gambling and smoking. In addition to pathological gambling and tobacco-cessation treatment, CLIENT would benefit from relapse prevention and sober living counseling.

D6) Current Recovery/Living Environment: 8 (High)

CLIENT currently lives alone in adequate housing, but may face eviction for nonpayment of rent, and her car may be repossessed. She is currently employed. CLIENT reports little, if any, stable, supportive social network beyond a neighbor and a friend at work. CLIENT reports her family relationships (son, daughter and two brothers who abuse alcohol) have been strained by her geographic isolation and gambling behavior. She reports feeling so lonely at times that she goes to the casino to be with people. CLIENT will benefit from assistance in developing social skills and a social support system.

Driving Dimensions: 1,3,5,6

Current driving dimensions are 1,3,5,6 based on intensity of gambling (DIM 1), mood disorder (DIM 3), relapse potential (DIM 5), and lack of social support (DIM 6).

Suicidality; Threat to Self/Others: 2 (Low)

CLIENT denies prior/current suicidal ideation/plan/attempt and denies family history of suicide/attempt. CLIENT currently appears to present a low risk (R1) of suicide, homicide, or threat to self or others.

Vulnerabilities/Strengths:

Vulnerabilities: CLIENT lacks stable social supports and lacks relapse prevention skills. CLIENT facing possible eviction and repossession of car for payment arrears.

Strengths: CLIENT appears to be willing to comply with treatment and appears to be concerned about her future, with internal motivation for treatment. CLIENT appears to be in relatively good health. CLIENT reports receiving employment income and continuing access to Veteran's Administration health care resources. CLIENT appeared to be focused, responsive and cooperative throughout the interview.

Assessment Instruments Used and Results:

CLIENT answered "Yes" to 8/10 questions on the DSM Gambling Screen, "Yes" to 15/17 questions on the NORC DSM-IV Screen for Gambling Problems (NODS), and "Yes" to 15/20 questions on the South Oaks Gambling Screen (SOGS). 5 or more "Yes" answers on any of the above instruments indicates probable Pathological Gambling. CLIENT answered "Yes" to 16/20 questions on the Gamblers Anonymous 20 Questions. 7 or more "Yes" answers on this survey suggests probable Compulsive Gambling. The Substance Abuse Subtle Screening Inventory (SASSI) was not administered during this assessment.

Clinical Impressions:

AXIS I:	312.31; 305.10 per self-report
AXIS II:	V71.09 No Diagnosis on Axis II
AXIS III:	311.00 prior Dx per self-report
AXIS IV:	Problems with primary support group, Economic problems
AXIS V:	GAF = 55 (current)

CLIENT reports a 10-year history of gambling, with associated social, interpersonal and legal difficulty. CLIENT appeared to be candid during the interview, and appears to be somewhat aware of the unsuccessful nature of her thinking and behavior patterns. CLIENT appears to believe she can complete a treatment program as well as attain and maintain abstinence. CLIENT presented promptly for the interview, with appropriate hygiene/grooming/attire, pleasant/ congruent mood/affect and was courteous/cooperative/responsive. CLIENT read all interview/ assessment paperwork without difficulty, completed necessary paperwork, and appears willing to comply with treatment.

This client meets diagnostic criteria for Pathological Gambling, as evidenced by maladaptive gambling behavior as indicated by five (or more) of the following: preoccupation with gambling; need to gamble with increasing amounts; repeated unsuccessful efforts to control, cut back, or stop gambling; restlessness/irritability when attempting to cut down/stop gambling; gambling to escape from problems or relieve dysphoric mood; after losing, "chasing" losses; lying to others to conceal extent of involvement with gambling; committing illegal acts to finance gambling; jeopardized/lost relationship/job/educational or career opportunity because of gambling; or reliance on others to relieve desperate gambling-related financial situation.

This client appears to be in the Preparation stage of change based on self-report. Based on frequency/intensity/duration of disorder and the severity of Dimensions One/Three/Five/Six, this client would benefit from GPPC Level II (Intensive Outpatient) treatment and care for Pathological Gambling.

Reports Made; Consents Given: At client request (with appropriate releases), copy of assessment with treatment recommendation mailed to RPGC Clinical Director on 5/31/07.

Provisional Treatment Plan; Discharge/Transition Criteria:
CLIENT to attend six weeks of Intensive Outpatient treatment for Pathological Gambling. CLIENT to attend aftercare weekly for up to one year following successful completion of Outpatient treatment. CLIENT to attend Gamblers Anonymous (GA) meetings at least three times weekly. CLIENT to seek smoking-cessation treatment.

Disposition/Follow-up/Appointment/Re-interview:
CLIENT agreed to attend RPGC Orientation at 5:30 pm Monday, June 4, and to begin IOP at that time. CLIENT also agreed to begin GA meeting attendance as part of the program.

Referrals:
CLIENT referred to Butts-Out Counseling, Tonopah, NV for smoking-cessation services.

Additional Information:
Hugh DeMann, M.A., LADC-S, CPGC-S, performed this assessment on 5/31/07 at Reputable Counseling Services, LLP, Tonopah, NV 89049.

Counselor Signature/Title: _____   Date: _____

Supervisor Signature/Title: _____   Date: _____

Chart Module

A Chart of Compulsive Gambling and Recovery

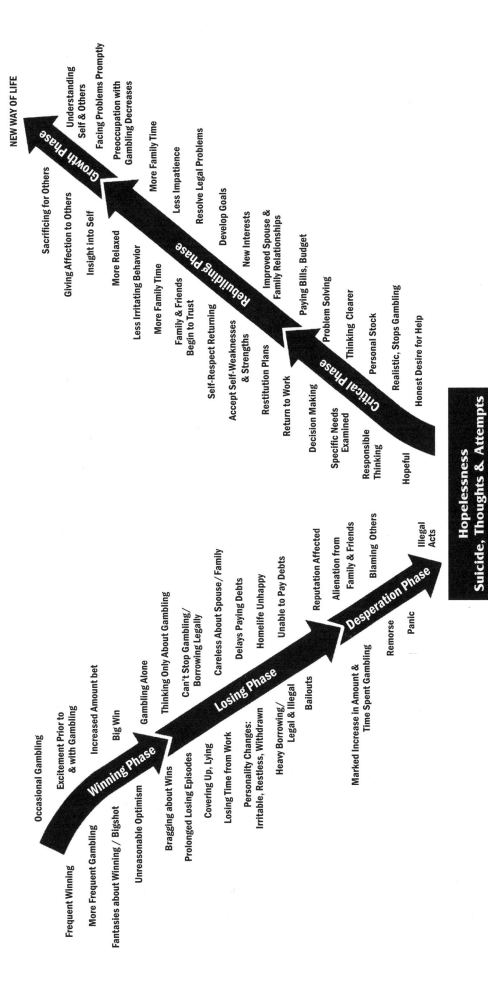

Robert L. Custer (1984) Profile of the pathological gambler. *The Journal of Clinical Psychiatry,* vol. 45 [12, Sec. 2]:35–38. Copyright 1984, Physicians PostGraduate Press. Adapted or reprinted by permission.

Stages of Change Model

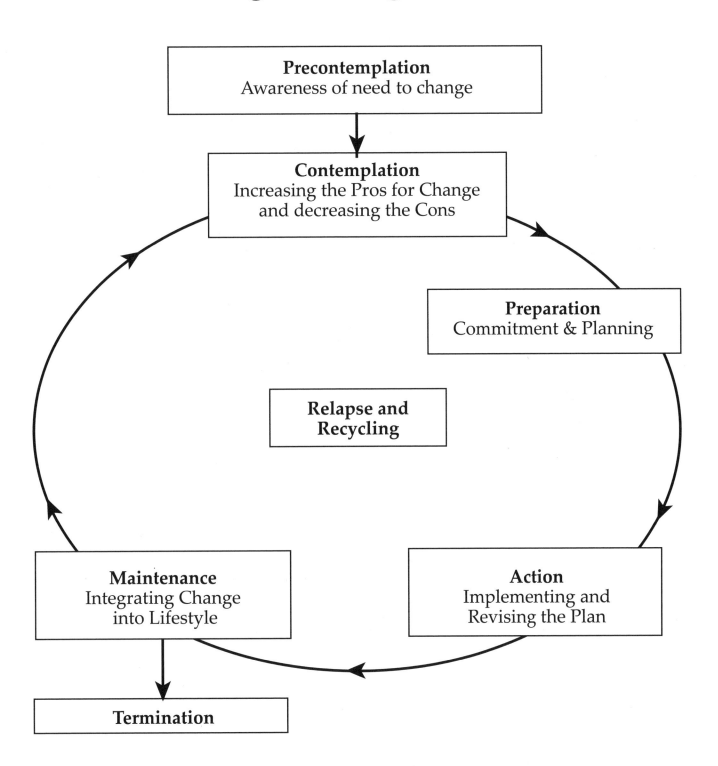

Precontemplation
Awareness of need to change

Contemplation
Increasing the Pros for Change
and decreasing the Cons

Preparation
Commitment & Planning

Relapse and
Recycling

Maintenance
Integrating Change
into Lifestyle

Action
Implementing and
Revising the Plan

Termination

DiClemente, Carlo C. (2006). *Addiction and Change:
How Addictions Develop and Addicted People Recover.*
Figure 2.1, page 30. New York: Guilford Publications, Inc.
Reprinted by permission. www.guilford.com

Preliminary Data Results

Some simple, preliminary statistical results of the initial 100 GPPC reports are presented on the following page. The initial results suggest gamblers currently seeking treatment in Northern Nevada rate at noticeable severity in Dimensions 1 (Frequency/Intensity/Duration of Disorder), 5 (Relapse or Continued Problem History or Potential), and 6 (Current Recovery/Living Environment). We have also included a simple listing of the characteristic demographic traits of the "average" problem gambler seeking treatment in Northern Nevada during the period we assembled the first 100 GPPC reports.

The GPPC Initiative is currently developing research questions and hypotheses related to the results and implications of these initial data in preparation for further research and publications. We solicit your support in this research initiative and in further efforts to improve and extend the body of knowledge concerning problem gambling and appropriate interventions.

First-year GPPC® Profile
(n=100)

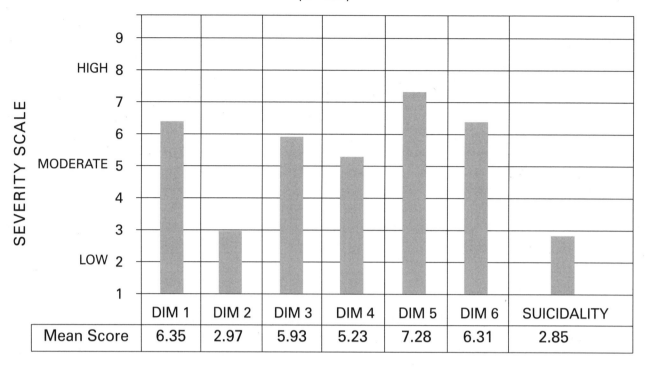

Mean Score	DIM 1	DIM 2	DIM 3	DIM 4	DIM 5	DIM 6	SUICIDALITY
	6.35	2.97	5.93	5.23	7.28	6.31	2.85

Dimension **1** — Frequency/Intensity/Duration of Disorder

Dimension **2** — Biomedical Conditions/Complications

Dimension **3** — Cognitive/Behavioral/Emotional Conditions

Dimension **4** — Readiness to Change

Dimension **5** — Relapse or Continued Problem History/Potential

Dimension **6** — Current Recovery/Living Environment

The "Average"
Northern-NV GPPC Gambler

- Age — 46
- Married
- Ethnicity — White
- Gender — (50/50)
- Non-drug User
- Nicotine — 50/50
- Employed
- Non-veteran
- Non-mandated

- Dim 1 — 6+   (Med)
- Dim 2 — 2+   (Low)
- Dim 3 — 5+   (Med)
- Dim 4 — 5+   (Med)
- Dim 5 — 7+   (High)
- Dim 6 — 6+   (Med)
- Suicidality — 2+   (Low)

References

American Psychiatric Association (2000). *Diagnostic and statistical manual of mental disorders* (4th ed., text revised). Washington, DC: Author.

American Society of Addiction Medicine (ASAM). (2001). *Patient placement criteria* (2nd ed., revised). Chevy Chase, MD: Author.

Gerstein, D., Murphy, S., Toce, M., Volberg, R., et al. (1999). *Gambling Impact and Behavior Study: Report to the National Gambling Impact Study Commission.* Chicago: National Opinion Research Center (NORC) at the University of Chicago. www2.norc.org/new/gamb-fin.htm

Lesieur, H. R. & Blume, S. B. (1987). The South Oaks Gambling Screen (SOGS): a new instrument for the identification of pathological gamblers. *American Journal of Psychiatry,* September, 144, 1184–88.

Johnson, E. E., Hamer, R. & Nora, R. M., et al. (1997). The lie/bet questionnaire for screening pathological gamblers. *Psychological Reports,* 80, 83–88.

Johnson, E. E., Hamer, R. & Nora, R. M. (1998). The lie/bet questionnaire for screening pathological gamblers: A follow-up study. *Psychological Reports,* 83(3 Part 2), 1219–24.

McCown, W. G., & Howatt, W. A. (2007). *Treating gambling problems.* New Jersey: John Wiley & Sons, Inc.

Merriam-Webster. (1993). *Webster's new encyclopedic dictionary.* New York: Black Dog and Leventhal Publishing.

National Council on Problem Gambling. (2009). *About problem gambling.* Retrieved from www.ncpgambling.org

National Institute on Drug Abuse (NIDA) (1999). National Institutes of Health (NIH). U.S. Department of Health and Human Services. *Principles of drug addiction treatment: A research-based guide.* Retrieved from www.drugabuse.gov/MedAdv/99/NR-1012.html

Nevada Council on Problem Gambling. (2005). *Understanding Problem Gambling.* www.nevadacouncil.org/under_prob_gam.php

San Francisco Suicide Prevention (2010). PLAIDS PALS. San Francisco, CA: www/sfsuicide/org

State of Nevada. (2007). *Nevada Administrative Code.*

State of Nevada. (2007). *Nevada Revised Statutes.*

Stinchfield, R., Winters, K.C., Botzet, A., Jerstad, S., & Breyer, J. (2007). Development and psychometric evaluation of the Gambling Treatment Outcome Monitoring System (GAMTOMS). *Psychology of Addictive Behaviors,* 21(2), 174–84.

Substance Abuse and Mental Health Services Administration. (2006). United States Department of Health and Human Services. *S.M.A.R.T. Treatment Planning,* Vol. 14(5). Retrieved from www.samhsa.gov/SAMHSA_News/Volume XIV_5/article2.htm

United States Code of Federal Regulations (2009). Title 42, Chapter 1, Subchapter A, Part 2: *Confidentiality of alcohol and drug abuse patient records*. Washington, DC: U.S. Government Printing Office.

Volberg, R. A. (2002). *Gambling and problem gambling in Nevada*. Northampton, MA: Gemini Research, Ltd.

Bibliography & Recommended Reading

American Psychiatric Association (2000). *Diagnostic and statistical manual of mental disorders* (4th ed., text revision). Washington, DC: Author.

American Psychiatric Association (1994). *Diagnostic and statistical manual of mental disorders* (4th ed.). Washington, DC: Author.

American Society of Addiction Medicine (ASAM). (2001). *Patient placement criteria* (2nd ed., revised). Chevy Chase, MD: Author.

Carlton, P. L., Manowitz, P., McBride, H., & Nora, R. M., (1987). Attention deficit disorder and pathological gambling. *Journal of Clinical Psychiatry, 48*(12), 487–88.

Ciarrocchi, J. W. (2002). *Counseling problem gamblers, A self-regulation manual for individual and family therapy.* San Diego: Academic Press.

Commission on Accreditation of Rehabilitation Facilities. (2009). *Behavioral health standards manual.* Washington, D.C.: Author.

Corey, M. S., & Corey, G. (1997). *Groups: Process and practice* (4th ed.). Pacific Grove: Brooks/Cole Publishing.

Custer, R., & Milt H. (1985). *When luck runs out: Help for compulsive gamblers and their families.* New York: Facts on File Publications.

Federman, E. J., Drebing, C. E., & Krebs, C. (2000). *Don't leave it to chance: A guide for families of problem gamblers.* Oakland: New Harbinger Publications, Inc.

Gambino, B. (2009). Should gambling be included in public health surveillance systems? *Journal of Gambling Issues, 23,* 156–76.

Gamblers Anonymous (2002). 12-Step Program. https://www.gamblersanonymous.org/recovery

Goldstein, L., Manowitz, P., Nora, R. M., Swartzburg, M., & Carlton, P. L. (1985). Differential EEG activation and pathological gambling. *Biological Psychiatry, 20*(11), 1145–253.

Grant, J. E. (2008). *Impulse control disorders: A clinician's guide to understanding and treating behavioral addictions.* New York: W.W. Norton & Company, Inc.

Grant, J. E. & Potenza, M. N. (2004). *Pathological gambling: A clinical guide to treatment.* Washington, DC: American Psychiatric Publishing, Inc.

Johnson, E. E., Hamer, R. M. & Nora, R. M. (1998). The lie/bet questionnaire for screening pathological gamblers: A follow-up study. *Psychological Reports, 83*(3 Part 2), 1219–24.

Johnson, E. E., & Nora, R. M. (1992). Does spousal participation in Gamblers Anonymous benefit compulsive gamblers? *Psychological Reports, 71*(3), 914.

Johnson, E. E., & Nora, R. M. (1992). The Rotter I-E scale as a predictor of relapse in a population of compulsive gamblers. *Psychological Reports, 70*(3), 691–96.

Korn, D. A., & Shaffer, H. J. (2004). Massachusetts Department of Public Health's *Practice guidelines for treating gambling-related problems: An evidence-based guide for clinicians.* https://www.masscompulsivegambling.org

Ladouceur, R., & Lachance, S. (2007). *Overcoming pathological gambling*. New York: Oxford University Press.

Ladouceur, R. & Shaffer, H. J. (2005). Treating problem gamblers: Working toward empirically supported treatment. *Journal of Gambling Studies, 21*(1), 1–4.

Ladouceur, R., Sylain, C., Boutin, C., & Doucet, C. (1998). *Understanding and treating the pathological gambler*. West Sussex, England: John Wiley & Sons, Ltd.

Lakey, C. E., Goodie, A. A., Lance, C. E., Stinchfield, R., & Winters, K. C. (2007). Examining DSM-IV criteria for pathological gambling: Psychometric properties and evidence from cognitive biases. *Journal of Gambling Studies, 23*(4), 479–98.

Levin, J. D. (1987). *Treatment of alcoholism and other addictions*. Northvale, NJ: Jason Inc.

Marlett, G. A., & Gordon, J. R. (Eds.). (1985). *Relapse prevention: Maintenance strategies in the treatment of addictive behaviors*. New York: Guilford Press.

Marotta, J. J. (1999). *Recovery from gambling problems with and without treatment*. Reno, NV: The University of Nevada, Reno.

Marotta, J. J., Cornelius, J. A., & Eadington, W. R. (Eds.) (2002). *The downside: Problem and pathological gambling*. Reno, NV: Institute for the Study of Gambling and Commercial Gaming Institute, The University of Nevada, Reno.

Masood, Z., Blaszczynski, A., & Turner, N. E. (Eds) (2008). *In the pursuit of winning: Problem gambling theory, research and treatment*. New York: Springer Science+Business Media, LLC.

Massachusetts Council on Compulsive Gambling, The Massachusetts Department of Public Health & The Division on Addictions at Harvard Medical School. (2001). *The results of a think tank on state-funded gambling treatment programs: A Massachusetts initiative*. Boston: Author.

McCown, W. G., & Howatt, W. A. (2007). *Treating gambling problems*. New Jersey: John Wiley & Sons, Inc.

Miller, W. R., & Rollnick, S. (2002). *Motivational interviewing: Preparing people for change*. (2nd ed.). New York: The Guilford Press.

Monti, P. M., Kadden, R. M., Rohsenow, D. J., Cooney, N. L., & Abrams, D. B. (2002). *Treating alcohol dependence: A coping skills training guide* (2nd ed.). New York: The Guilford Press.

National Council on Problem Gambling. (2009). *About problem gambling*. Retrieved from www.ncpgambling.org

National Endowment for Financial Education. (2000). *Personal financial strategies for the loved ones of problem gamblers*. Denver: Author.

National Gambling Impact and Policy Commission. (1999). *The National gambling impact study commission: Final report*. Washington, DC: Author.

National Institute of Drug Abuse (NIDA) (1999). *Principles of drug addiction treatment: A research-based guide* (No. 99-4180). Rockville, Maryland: National Institutes of Health.

National Research Council. Commission on Behavioral and Social Sciences and Education. Committee on the Social and Economic Impact of Pathological Gambling and Committee on Law and Justice (1999). *Pathological gambling: A critical review*. Washington, DC: National Academy Press.

Nevada Council on Problem Gambling. *Understanding Problem Gambling.* www/nevadacouncil.org

Nora, R.M. (1989). Inpatient treatment programs for pathological gamblers. In H.J. Shaffer, S.A. Stein, B. Gambino, & T.N. Cummings (Eds.). *Compulsive gambling: Theory, research, and practice* (127-134). Lexington, MA: Lexington Books.

Nora, R.M. (1986). Substance abuse, mental illness, and pathological gambling. *The American Journal of Psychiatry, 143*(4), 558–59.

Petry, N.M. (2005). *Pathological gambling: Etiology, comorbidity, and treatment.* Washington, DC: American Psychological Association.

Potenza, M.N., & Winters, K.C. (2003). The neurobiology of pathological gambling: Translating research findings into clinical advances. *Journal of Gambling Studies, 19*(1), 7–10.

Prochaska, J.O., & DiClemente, C.C. (1984). *Transtheoretical therapy: Crossing the traditional boundaries of therapy.* Malabar, FL: Krieger.

Stinchfield, R., Kushner, M.G., & Winters, K.C. (2005). Alcohol use and prior substance abuse treatment in relation to gambling problem severity and gambling treatment outcome. *Journal of Gambling Studies, 21*(3), 273–97.

Stinchfield, R., Winters, K.C., Botzet, A., Jerstad, S., & Breyer, J. (2007). Development and psychometric evaluation of the Gambling Treatment Outcome Monitoring System (GAMTOMS). *Psychology of Addictive Behaviors, 21*(2), 174–84.

Shaffer, H.J., LaBrie, R.A., LaPlante, D.A. Kidman, R.C., & Korn, D.A. (2002). *The Iowa department of public health gambling treatment services: Four years of evidence.* Boston: Harvard Medical School Division on Addictions. www.divisiononaddictions.org

State of Nevada (2007). *Nevada Administrative Code.*

State of Nevada (2007). *Nevada Revised Statutes.*

Sylvain, C., Ladouceur R., & Boisvert, J. (1997). Cognitive and behavioral treatment of pathological gambling: A controlled study. *Journal of Counseling and Clinical Psychology, 65*(5), 727–32.

Taber, J.I. (2008). *Addictions Anonymous.* Ingersoll Literary Productions.

Taber, J.I. (2001). *In the shadow of chance: The pathological gambler.* Bluffton: Ex-Gambler Services.

United States Code of Federal Regulations (2009). Title 42, Chapter 1, Subchapter A, Part 2: *Confidentiality of alcohol and drug abuse patient records.* Washington, DC: U.S. Government Printing Office.

United States Department of Health and Human Services (December 1999). National Institutes of Health. National Institute on Drug Abuse. *NIDA Notes, 14*(5).

United States Department of Health and Human Services (2006). *Substance abuse: Clinical issues in intensive outpatient treatment.* A Treatment Improvement Protocol, TIP 47. Rockville: Substance Abuse and Mental Health Services Administration, Center for Substance Abuse Treatment. https://download.ncadi.samhsa.gov/prevline/pdfs/TIP_47.pdf

Velasquez, M.M., Mauer, G.G., Couch, C., & DiClemente, C.C. (2001). *Group treatment for substance abuse: A stages-of-change therapy manual.* New York: The Guilford Press.

Volberg, R. A. (2002). *Gambling and problem gambling in Nevada.* Northampton, MA: Gemini Research, Ltd.

Winters, K. C., & Kushner, M. G. (2003) Treatment issues pertaining to pathological gamblers with a comorbid disorder. *Journal of Gambling Studies, 19*(3), 261–77.

Yalom, I. D. (1995). *The theory and practice of group psychotherapy* (4th ed.). New York: Basic Books.